Dedication

To my Tabitha...

Proverbs 31:10-31

Preface

April 19, 1995 – 7:02 AM PST

"A truck bomb detonated in Oklahoma City killing 168 innocent
Americans including women and children. Initial intelligence and
news reports indicated that an up-and-coming violent Domestic
Terrorist movement was responsible for the bombing"

Militia – Sovereign Citizen Movement

The Assignment

"No young man ever thinks he shall die."
William Hazlitt

"Bird3 to Tower. Inbound with the *king unit*, route, mark time," I heard over my headset as the helicopter descended upon the rooftop of the bank tower. As I remembered that the bank tower was the City's tallest building, dwarfing the helipad from the air, my stomach skipped as the pilot negotiated what I would consider a perfect landing on a postage stamp. *What's a king unit? Is he referring to me?*

"Roger that, Bird3, route, time marked. King unit, safe travels," a robotic voice echoed from the tower.

"Sir, standby until we clear you to exit the bird. Once clear, walk across the gangway to the north and through the door. Your handlers will be waiting for you there, sir. Do you have any questions?" The pilot's voice echoed over my headset. I believe I recognized his voice from my last flight, but I wasn't certain.

"No, I'm good. Thank you," I responded, never certain what to say or not to say during this transition of my double life.

"Sir, don't forget to exit straight out of the bird. Cole will grab your stuff," the pilot replied, never turning to look at me.

"Understood, sir. Thanks for the ride."

"Godspeed, son." I saw him perform a quick hand salute but his face remained hidden behind the dark face shield of his helmet.

Cole, riding in the second seat, opened the door and the rotor noise was deafening as he handed me my bag. He motioned with his right hand, a signal I recognized from my academy days (open hand, fingers spread wide with a ninety-degree bend in his elbow) towards the gangway on the north side of the building. With a slight nod, I gave him a thumbs up as the rotor wash blew Los Angeles debris in my eyes. After a quick hand salute, Cole turned and reboarded the bird. The sheer *coolness* of what I had just

4

experienced came over me briefly, but my mind quickly turned back to Liz and the gravity of the Chief's request. Just one hour ago, Liz and I had been enjoying life together for the first time since I had gone undercover – we hadn't seen each other for several months – only to be interrupted by Mick, a guy I had never seen before, telling me our getaway had been cut short because some crazy nut job had detonated a truck bomb outside of the Federal Building in Oklahoma City, killing 168 people. Then I was told it was my job to see if there was a connection with or problem in the City with a militia group, starting tonight by attending a meeting in Bakersfield which I knew nothing about. WTF…

"Steven, how was your conjugal visit?" Al asked in a perverted tone as I walked through the doorway. He was alone this time, which was shocking to me. I ignored his inappropriate comment, but it set the tone for the mental state that I needed to be in.

Al cleared his throat, most likely from years of smoking. "Hey this just came down from the Chief. Have you seen the news lately?"

"No, but that guy Mick filled me in… Mick. Mick was his name, right?" I asked.

"Yes, Mick is his name," Al answered, bothered by my trivial question. "Listen up! A truck bomb was detonated on Monday in Oklahoma City and we just received info that the militia movement was behind the attack. We don't have any intel on this these guys and the FBI is useless. The Chief is on the Captain's ass to see if we have a militia movement here in the City," Al continued.

"Okay, but what does that have to do with me?" I asked.

"Your assignment just got changed, kid, from the KKK to militias. Chief wants this to be our top priority. There is a prominent militia speaker, named Bobo, speaking tonight in Bakersfield. I need you to go," he said in a no bullshit tone.

"Seriously," I said, as I paused, trying to figure out what a militia was; I remembered reading about militias during the Revolutionary War, but that was the last time I had ever heard or thought about them.

"There are still militias around? What are they all about?" I asked.

"I haven't been briefed by our analyst Trip yet, so I really don't know much. What I do know is that they blew up a truck bomb in Oklahoma City two days ago and the Chief is on our ass to track these fuckers down. I haven't seen our Captain this worked up in a long time. He called me up yelling and told me to make sure we have a *bird* at this meeting tonight. Guess what… you're the only *bird* that fits the profile. So, it's on you, kid."

"Al, I don't think I can do that tonight," I said nervously.

"Well don't think. Just do what the fuck I tell you. Listen there's a possibility that there is going to be a media presence there because of the bombing. You are to stay away from all cameras. Just blend in. There will probably be tables set up and I want you to buy a couple things of literature and pick up some pamphlets. That's it. You got it!" Al's voice grew clearer and louder.

As I processed the enormity of Al's request several questions passed through my brain like a news ticker tape. "Okay, how much should I spend? What do you want me to buy? Should I talk to anyone? Is there anything specific that you're looking for?"

Al cut me off, "Steven, relax! Just go to the damn meeting. I don't know how much money you're going to spend. Just go to the fucking meeting, listen to what he has to say and try and remember a few names.

6

That's it…page me the all-clear signal when you get back. That's it. Fuck!"

"Yes, sir, I got it, but shouldn't I be briefed on this group? Who's my target?"

Al cut me off again and his voice was now clear of all phlegm. "Steven, don't call me sir! Fuck, don't they teach you *birds* anything anymore? I already gave you your instructions. There is no manual for this. Figure it out! When you get home, page me and we'll debrief," he said as his frustration built.

As we completed the exchange of my double life credentials, I didn't feel prepared to go to the meeting. I knew this day had been coming and at least in my head I'd felt that I would be better prepared. Simple stuff, like what do I wear to a militia convention? I felt like a teenage girl getting dressed for her first date. As I left the Bank Tower parking lot, I stopped to grab a quick bite to eat at the Beef Bowl in the Valley. Probably not the healthiest choice, but it was fast, filling, and the taste was actually not too bad. I just hoped the beef or beef substitute wouldn't upset my sensitive stomach.

As I pulled into the Bakersfield Convention's parking lot that night, I was shocked at how many cars there were: I was thinking, are you sure this isn't a Bon Jovi or Boys II Men concert? Small media presence… Hmm; I wondered what Al's definition of *small* was because it looked like every major network was represented here. I guessed he forgot to mention the *protesters* that were yelling at me when I drove into the parking lot; one sign read, "Militia Men are baby killers!" My hands were already sweating and I hadn't even walked inside yet. As I walked into the building, my heart rate began to quicken, but I was somewhat surprised after entering the building. I didn't see a bunch of GI Joe wannabe machine-gun, grenade-carrying militia members dressed in camouflage with face paint. Sure, there were a few of the GI Joe types, but the majority of the people looked like your everyday mom and pop lined up at a buffet line in Vegas.

The arena was a typical auditorium housing several thousand people. In the lobby area several tables were set up each promoting a different philosophy or selling some type of survivalist gear or rhetoric. These were not your typical products; these I had never heard about before. But most of the tables were offering some sort of proof either via books, photographs or literature regarding a government conspiracy referred to as "The New World Order."

As the event started, I wandered my way up to the top of the arena, isolating myself on the high ground, figuring I would have a good observation point. The arena was jam-packed. Just as the event MC walked onto the stage a semi-attractive woman began to make her way up the stairs towards me. Flashback moment: You know when you're sitting on an airplane before takeoff and you're staring at all of the passengers walking the gauntlet towards your aisle. I am generally repeating a small prayer in my head similar to this, "Please don't be in the middle seat, please." However, there have been a few occasions where I was praying, "please God, just this once... sit, sit, please sit."

She had dark brown hair about shoulder length with a slight wave, 5 6", 115lbs with nice firm breasts; not too big or too small. She was wearing blue jeans, a tight OD green shirt, with black military style boots, approximately thirty years of age, but God had spent a little more time on her. As she reached the top of the arena, she turned down the same aisle that I was sitting in and sat two seats to my left. As she passed me, I picked up a clean soapy smell, but no perfume. Most likely ivory soap.

As the key note speaker, Bobo, began his introductions and announcements, I noticed several of the attendees appeared to be taking notes feverishly, but I hadn't brought a pen or note pad. I began to count the rows in my head to get an approximate number of attendees and scan the crowd to see if I could identify who was who in the crowd. There were two exits near me at the top of the stadium and I had parked my car near the Side 2 emergency exit. The speaker, Bobo, was talking about a government conspiracy as I continued my *safety checks*.

"Excuse me...Excuse me..." a firm voice calls out.

I saw movement coming towards me out of my left peripheral, and turned my body to the left to address the possible threat. It was the Ivory Soap Woman.

"I didn't mean to startle you, sorry about that," she said with a perplexed look on her face.

"Oh, no you didn't startle me," I stumbled to explain my nerves. "Well, I mean, I guess you did... And I must have been zoning out because this stuff is crazy what he's talking about. This chip thing, I don't even know what it is but it sounds insane," I said as I gathered my composure.

Ivory Woman shifted her body weight towards me, exposing a tattoo on her wrist, but I didn't recognize it. "Bobo's talking about a micro-chip that the United Nations has developed under the *New World Order* to be planted into our bodies in order to track us. Once they have this established, they can always find you and if you don't go along with the *New World Order* you will be tracked down and killed. The government wants you to believe that it's just an easy way for you to shop, bank, and identify yourself, but we know the truth," she said, nodding her head.

I mirrored her body movements just as I was trained. "Really? They can't do that, can they? I knew the government was up to stuff but I didn't know that one." Acknowledging her point.

An awkward silence fell briefly between us as she appeared to be sizing me up. I was doing the same to her, wondering if this was just another JT test.

"Steven…" I extend my hand out to hers.

"Sheila…" She extended her hand to mine, making direct eye contact. Gripped my hand firmly, like a man, and slightly turned her wrist counter-clockwise, to dominate the handshake, tightening her grip ever so slightly.

"Are you from around here?" I asked, trying to release my handshake. But Sheila didn't release her grip and continued to look into my eyes just slightly longer. The extended handshake and eye contact was not awkward but noticeable for me.

Sheila released my hand. "You have cop eyes," she said.

I chuckled nervously. "Never heard that one before, but thanks, I think. I wish I had yours, they're beautiful."

Sheila's head turned away. "Thanks…got them from my mom." She shifted her body away from mine.

"I got mine from my dad. He wasn't a cop, but he served in the army; close enough I guess." I settled back into my seat.

Sheila and I talked throughout Bobo's presentation. Sheila was very knowledgeable about the movement and seemed very dedicated to the militia. As we talked she began interrogating me indirectly, but I recognized it. I played into the role and connected a lot easier with a woman, especially a semi-attractive one. As Sheila and I talked, she educated me on the current issues within the militia movement. I flirted and tried to charm her the best I knew how, but by her smile I could tell she wasn't having it. I wondered if I should try and ask her out for dinner, but I was unclear if that was against *the rules* or how my girlfriend back home would feel about that.

The meeting continued for approximately two hours. Bobo was a talented, charismatic speaker. He knew how to motivate people and he provided a sense of leadership and direction, which the militia movement appeared to lack at that time. An occasional chant would echo throughout the auditorium: "Bobo, Bobo, Bobo."

His speaking style seemed to manipulate people and twist their minds into a frenzy, causing them to believe that the world was going to be taken over by a ONE WORLD GOVERNMENT CONSPIRACY under the UNITED NATIONS. Bobo offered special training called S.P.I.K.E training for militia members in order for them to get *prepared* to fight this invisible enemy. His claim to fame was being a Green Beret in the army which he now applied to sell his training to the militia movement. Bobo appeared to be a wolf dressed in sheep's clothing to me, but in hindsight he was strictly a brilliant business salesman who capitalized on people's paranoia and dissatisfaction with the government, and not a true dedicated militia man down with the cause.

As the meeting came to an end, I walked down to the front tables with Sheila. Sheila said, "I want to introduce you to a few of my friends." We walked over to the west side of the building towards a group of men dressed in full army fatigues with military insignias on their collars and patches representing rank on their uniforms. Ahhh, finally, the GI Joe wannabe's I was expecting, I thought. A bunch of older gents with pot bellies hanging over wrinkled army fatigues, unshaven, with clear disheveled looks. It wasn't my idea of what a "domestic terrorist" would look like. My initial thoughts were that these gents couldn't run down to the local store to get a cup of ice cream, much less be bad ass terrorists.

Sheila introduced me to "Commander Joel" of the KLC militia. Joel was about 5'5", 155lbs, with silver hair parted to one side and a thick mustache. Approximately sixty-five years of age, years he didn't wear very well, and soft spoken. He didn't seem very intimidating or a major threat, let alone capable of mass destruction like the Oklahoma Bombing. Sheila told Joel about me and that I was interested in joining the militia movement. Joel introduced me to another man named Paul who I was told was in charge of "Militia Personnel." Paul was a "Captain" rank within the militia, and his body odor quickly overcame me, almost like a repellent. He was younger than the others, about forty years old, but his pot belly would make Santa Claus jealous. He had long stringy, blond hair and a particularly large stain on his shirt. Paul took down my name, address, and phone number and told me he would be in touch.

Sheila and I walked around to some of the booths and she pointed out some books that I should read. The first thing she told me to get was a book called *The Turner Diaries*. I bought the book and some other literature just as my handler had instructed me to then I decided it was time to go.

"Sheila, I have to go, but when am I going to see you again?" I asked as I reached out to shake her hand.

"You have a long way to go before you see me again, Steven," she said as she looked down at my extended hand. "We don't say goodbye like White America, Steven." Ignoring my extended hand, her heels snapped together as she extended her right hand to her temple, saluting me. "DEATH TO THE NEW WORLD ORDER, STEVEN!"

I wasn't quite sure what to do, so I awkwardly smiled, waved and walked away. Was I supposed to salute her back? Give her my phone number? I turned back, looking over my shoulder at Sheila, similar to when I'd purchased my first car, puzzled at how she could appear to be so normal, then just sheer crazy.

What did I get myself into? I thought.

I drove home pondering the conference, trying to understand what the attendees' motives were. Were these people really responsible for the Oklahoma City truck bomb? Had a future bomber possibly been in attendance with me? As I attempted to psychoanalyze the attendees and my performance on my long drive home, the only conclusions that I came up with were that I was mentally exhausted. The mental exhaustion of keeping up with two different identities, making sure their lives didn't collide; what was truth and what was a lie; gathering all of the new information, and trying to suppress my natural tendencies had all taken a toll that I couldn't explain.

Always operating on high alert...

Trying not to expose my real identity...

Answer to my real name or give off any clues...

Trying to remember my background story...

Observing everything that was going on, trying to identify potential targets...

Gathering physical descriptions, names, license plates, etc…

All without writing anything down, just as I was trained. My brain was on mental overload.

As I arrived back at my apartment, I just needed a moment to decompress before I checked in with Al, so I decided to lie down on my couch, the one remaining comfort from my real life, and turn on the television.

Beep, Beep, Beep, Beep, Beep!

The sharp piercing sound ricocheted off the walls of my apartment, awakening me from a deep sleep. Disorientated, I tried to find the source of the piercing sound, quickly realizing it was my lifeline, my pager. Jumping up, I scoured my pants which I had left on my living room floor, and grabbed my pager. *930-3333*, it read.

"Damn it!" I murmured, realizing my catastrophic mistake.

"930" was Al's call sign and "3333" meant code three, which in police lingo is an emergency. I still hadn't rung in with Al, having fallen asleep by accident.

I ran out of my apartment, jumped into my car and drove down to the local 7-Eleven to use the phone there, keeping my op-sec protocols in place. I jumped out of the car and grabbed the handset of the payphone. The handle was wet and had a strange odor as I brought it up to my ear. There was no dial tone…

"Damn it!" I yelled.

I saw a CVS pharmacy across the street with a bank of pay phones. I ran across the street, dodging between cars stopped at a red light. *Honk, Honk…* One of the drivers let me know their dissatisfaction with my efforts.

Beep, Beep, Beep… This time my pager was displaying 930-333333333. I grabbed the phone and heard a strong dial tone as I reached for the quarters in my pocket.

"Damn it! This is not my day!" Realizing that I had forgotten to grab any quarters, I dropped the phone and ran inside the CVS store to get change.

Ring, Ring… I tried to slow my breathing.

"What the fuck is your problem. You have been home for two hours and you haven't checked in!" Al yelled into the phone as I imagined that blood vessel on the right side of his neck bulging.

"Al… Al, I'm sorry. I fell asleep," I said, realizing as the words came out of my mouth that they weren't the best choice of words.

"You fucking fell asleep!" Al interrupted me mid-sentence, now screaming, me imagining his neck vein had reached full capacity in my exhausted mind.

"Un-fucking believable, you fell asleep." Al laughed out loud in disgust. "Let me get this straight, you go out on your very first op and you go home without checking in and fall asleep? Jesus, what kind of *birds* are they training these days. This is what JT gives me. A fucking *bird* that falls asleep."

"Al it wasn't like that…" I tried to explain, but he interrupted me mid-sentence again.

"What do you mean it wasn't like that? Did you get your little blanky first or a cup of hot tea, maybe turn on a movie, before you fucking fell asleep? Is that what it was like?" Al continued to scream as his voice cracked with anger.

Realizing that every time I opened my mouth with feeble explanations of my screw-up were just making it worse, I changed tactics and just took the *Fifth*, remaining silent, taking my medicine as Al continued to dose it out for the next ten minutes. We hung and then I walked across the street back to the 7-Eleven and bought myself a Big Gulp Dr. Pepper and a large bag of Funyuns to drown my disappointment.

An analytical person by nature, but not one who dwells on any issues too long, in this particular case I couldn't get it out of my mind. I didn't know what to do. Normally, I would call up my girlfriend, a buddy or someone from my family, discuss my issue, then I would be done and move on. How did I do that in this new life? I couldn't talk to my *gangster buddies* for obvious reasons, my real *boys* from home didn't even know what I was doing or where I was at, my parents and family were in the same boat, I couldn't call my handler because he was pissed off, and I couldn't call JT's crew or I would piss Al off even more. But mentally, I recognized that I was going through a little identity crisis as I took another drink of my Dr. Pepper. I just didn't know how to handle it. So, I did what every boy does I guess… Called my mommy, lol.

Ring, ring, ring… "Hello," a familiar female voice answered.

"Ma?" I said, trying not to touch my mouth to the phone receiver back outside the 7-Eleven.

"Mac! Is that you? Are you okay? What's wrong?" My mom's voice was inflected with a mixture of excitement and fear.

"Yeah, I'm fine, Ma. I thought I would just call and see how you are," I said.

"What time is it, Mac? Are you sure you're okay? You don't sound like you're okay."

16

"Ma, Ma…" I interrupted her rapid line of questioning. "Ma, can we not do this? I just want to talk. Can we just talk and please don't ask me anything."

My mom hesitated, but got the message. "Okay, sure, of course, let's just talk… So let me see, your sister got a new dog, I don't know why she got a new dog. I don't think she realizes how much work a puppy is. Mac, a new puppy is like having a child…"

I just sat there on a pay phone listening to my mom's rambling, not saying a word, putting in more quarters until eventually I was broke.

"You have two minutes remaining," a robotic voice interrupted my mom's rambling.

"Ma, I have to go, but thank you. Say hi to everyone and I love you." Tears began to well up in my eyes.

"Mac… Mac, promise me you're okay and call me anytime. I promise I won't ask you any questions. We'll just talk, okay?"

"You have twenty seconds remaining," the robotic voice interrupted.

"Love you, Ma, bye." As I hung up the phone, I began to sob uncontrollably. Here I was, an undercover cop working for the anti-terrorism department, sobbing after hanging up a payphone at a 7-Eleven in the middle of the ghetto. Some fearless operator I am, I thought.

Saturday 0330 hours

Ring… Ring… Ring… Ring… Ring… I heard the phone ringing in my dreams. Suddenly the ringing stopped.

Ring... Ring... Ring... Ring... Ring... I sat up as I realized that it was my home phone and not in my dreams. Nothing ever good comes from a phone call at 3:30 in the morning. Besides, no one had my phone number. I grabbed my pager from my night stand, a blue milk crate turned on its end with a pillow case draped over the top, but the pager display was empty.

"Hello?" I answered groggily.

"Steven, this is Paul from the KLC militia. Were you sleeping?" he asked in a chipper voice.

"Who is this? What time is it?"

"Steven, it's Paul from KLC militia. Sorry to wake you, I'll call you later."

The phone went dead as I checked the phone receiver to see what phone number he was calling me from. *Blocked.*

"What the heck..."

I stumbled back to my bed, but my mind began to race. This guy had just called me at 0330 hours. What was that about? Should I call my handlers right now or wait to let them know? Well... in order for me to call my handlers I would have to go back to the CVC pharmacy and page them from the pay phone then wait. I wasn't doing that. I was going back to bed. These conversations in my head continued for the next two hours as the sun breached the vertical blinds.

0800 hours – I went out for my breakfast because I had to work nights at the department store; Maria was working.

"Good morning, Steven!" she said when she saw me, "Coffee? Oh, I'm sorry, I forgot you don't drink coffee. It's tea... right?" She walked me

18

to my table, the third table on the west side near the kitchen entrance where there was a back door leading to an alleyway.

"Thank you, Maria. Do you have a newspaper left over?" I asked as I sat down.

Beep, beep... I paused the piercing sound quickly. 930-1111. It was Al, returning my page to him earlier.

"Maria, I'll take my usual and I'll be right back," I told her on my way to the pay phones just outside. As I dialled Al up on the phone, I couldn't help but wonder what kind of mood he was going to be in as he answered the phone.

"Steven, what's up. Everything okay?" Al asked.

"Yeah, all is good, but I'm just giving you a head's up, that Paul guy from the militia called me last night," I explained.

"What guy? What militia?" Al's voice heightened.

"Ummm... that Paul guy I met at the militia convention you sent me to," I answered.

"Oh wow, that was fast! What time did he call you?" Al's tone began to settle.

"He called me at 3:30 in the morning. I wasn't happy."

"Interesting, they were checking on you. Much quicker than those KKK assholes. Their Op Sec will most likely be on another level than we've seen previously."

"Wait, what do you mean? What's going on? I'm a little confused."

"You see, the FBI always plants undercovers at these types of meetings, but their UCs are generally just part time, during working hours, you know. They aren't full time *birds* living the life like you. This guy Paul was most likely checking to see if you really were sleeping in your

19

apartment and not some part time FBI plant. It's part of their op sec. The white power guys normally wait to start their op sec after a couple of meetings. These guys aren't playing around." I heard a little chuckle in Al's voice.

"What do I do now or what happens next?" I asked.

"You just do you. Don't worry, they'll get ahold of you. Make sure your shit is tight, you hear me. This thing just got real," Al said.

I walked back inside and Maria waved at me, smiling. "Steven, I put your food on your table and I put a napkin over it so the flies won't get it." She grabbed two more orders from the kitchen as I quickly looked towards the front to see what Alphabet rating this Denny had. A solid *B*, not bad for the ghetto.

Al was right, Paul called me back later that day and invited me to an official KLC militia meeting the following week at a church approximately 125 miles from my place, outside the city limits.

Meeting No. 1

I had to leave work early that day, "sick" of course, in order to make the one-and-a-half-hour drive to make the meeting on time. Vince Lombardi's rules had been ingrained into my head by my father throughout my younger years. All of my training and sacrifice was about to be *tested* – or maybe a better phrase was *pay off?* The drive was surprisingly quick. The LA traffic was kind; the radio station was vibing with oldies but goodies. Bon Jovi, Garth Brooks and Restless Heart. I wasn't thinking much about my debut as a *bird*; I was more concerned about my car making the drive without a mechanical hiccup. As I approached the church, I noticed two older gents sitting outside at a check-in table; "Name, rank and militia?" the older of the two gents asked me.

"Hey guys, my name is Steven. I don't belong to a militia, but Paul invited me."

"Paul Orion, from KLC?" the other older gent asked me.

"I think so. I'm sorry. I'm really bad with names," I said.

"Okay, here you are," the first older gent said as I saw him pointing to my name on a piece of paper with approximately five other names. I saw "Don Morris" just below my name and committed it to memory.

"Are you an agent of the government?" the second older gent asked me, sounding like he was reading from a set of questions.

"I'm sorry what?" I asked.

The second older gent's head raised up and he looked at me in dismay. "Are you a cop or a government agent, kid?" he asked me again with authority.

"Oh sorry, I didn't understand what you were asking me. No sir, I am not."

He continued with his line of questioning:

"Are you armed?"

"No sir."

"Do you have any recording devices on you?"

"No sir."

"Do you believe in the New World Order?"

I paused… "I don't know what that it is," I said.

"Okay, you're good. Put this around your neck," he handed me a laminated card hanging from a lanyard. "Sit in the first three rows only," the first older gent said.

The *church*, a converted warehouse, was similar to an old YMCA gym: white folding chairs stacked in rows of ten, two columns wide with one grey chair in the third row of the west column. A 4' x 8' raised homemade stage had been constructed out of plywood, covered with green outdoor carpet perched in front of the chairs. A standing microphone, similar to what Elvis Presley used to use, had been placed on the makeshift stage, a cord extending to a single speaker set off to the side. The windows of the church were covered with aluminum foil, unlike the stained glass I was accustomed to seeing back home. The building was cold and lacked anything descriptive or immediately identifiable in the religious realm. Two flags stood erect in the far corner, one an early iteration of the American flag, but not one that I recognized, and the second a "don't tread on me flag." *Sit in the front three rows*, I chuckled to myself as I walked towards the front of the church counting the rows in my head. Twenty rows times ten, that's two hundred, times two. Four hundred people in this joint? No way. These militia boys had the same childish rules that cops did, requiring all rookies to sit in the front row. Were they going to throw paper at the back of my head next? The irony...

I continued my op-sec. Sentry posted at the 1-2 corner with a long rifle that I didn't recognize and another at the 3-4 corner with what looked like an M-16, slung. My seat was in the middle of the second row which went against all of my cop instincts and training. I didn't see any obvious exits except the door located in the back of the church where I had entered. As the room began to fill with attendees, I still didn't have my escape route(s) locked down. A camcorder had been placed off to the side recording everyone as they entered the church. I didn't see a fire alarm pull anywhere.

22

The 3-4 corner sentry appeared very comfortable with his weapon system; his right arm was folded across the butt stock of the weapon, with his left hand folded on top of the carry handle. He was set up as a right-handed shooter. The weapon didn't have any glass on it used for aiming and the safety was in a parallel position, indicating that it was on. A thirty round magazine was secured in the magazine well, with what looked like a secondary weapon on his right hip, a Berretta, not sure of the caliber. His face was relaxed but he was in a *go zone,* actively observing the crowd as they entered and scouring the room in a systematic pattern. I didn't see any comms and he wasn't wearing any body armor.

The 1-2 sentry looked like a soup sandwich cop that I'd worked with once on morning watch and out of his element. *If this goes south, he's my target. I can take him out. I just don't know that weapon system. Shit, Mac, you're going to have to figure it out. I should move seats to get closer to him. That's too risky. You're fine. Just chill and don't draw any attention to yourself by moving seats. Find the bathroom, Mac. Maybe there's another out.* My mind raced with options.

I walked the four sides of the church, headed towards the back where I'd entered, but I didn't see a bathroom or any other out. I could feel my anxiety increasing.

"Steven, can I help you?" a man asked me as he stepped in front of me, blocking my path.

"Hi, I'm Steven… oh, I guess you already knew that. I was just looking for a bathroom?"

"Hey, Steven, yes, I know who you are. You're one of the new recruits that the other Paul recommended. My name is Corporal Paul Freeman and I run logistics. If you just head back outside the doors and make a left there's a water closet out there," he said as he motioned me towards the door.

Hmm, water closet. Nobody says that where I'm from. He can't be from around here, I thought to myself.

"Awesome. Nice to meet you too, Paul," I said, extending my hand.

"You too, Steven, and you can call me Corporal," Paul replied as we shook hands.

"This meeting will come to rise," I heard as I walked towards the door. "Let's start with the Pledge of Allegiance followed by the oath." A deep voice echoed throughout the church.

I felt as if all eyes were on me as I walked towards the doors and that everyone knew that I was really a cop. Why else would Paul block my path? Why was the one sentry fixated on my position the entire time? My mind began to race again and my hands were sweating profusely, showing my nerves, but I was almost at the exit. *Mac, just get outside. Just get to your car and get the hell out of here. They know. This is not good. Get out!* My mind began to play tricks on me. *Mac, you're fine. These old, white trash, hillbillies don't know shit. Just relax. You're fine. Go to the water closet. Who calls a bathroom a water closet? Get your crap together and get back in there.*

As I breached the threshold of the door, exiting the church, a sense of relief overcame me; I spotted my car off to my three o'clock and the water house off to my nine o'clock. I froze. My mind was clouded with fear that I had never experienced before. It was as if my legs had stopped working. My brain was telling them to walk, but they felt extremely *heavy* and disobedient. Finally, my legs began to move again as I walked towards the water closet. Step after step, I finally made it. I stood in the water closet

24

arguing with myself, silently of course. *Mac, you need to get back in the game! Mac, you need to leave. You are not ready for this. Get out of here while you still can.* The arguments continued in my head until it hit me and I started to laugh out loud. What hit me you may ask? Ray Ramirez hit me. Ray and I had worked together a few times back on patrol. I loved working with Ray. We just clicked. Ray used to call out to me from time to time generally when we would pull up to a stop light in south Los Angeles.

"Hey, Mac? Who's that guying talking to?" he'd ask, referring to a 5150 standing on the corner talking to his imaginary friend.

"Who?" I asked.

"That 5150 standing right there!"

"I don't know, sir. He's crazy."

"Why do you say that he's crazy? Maybe he really is talking to someone and you just can't see them…" Ray would continue as we argued who was right or wrong over the next hour.

My laughter allowed me to refocus and exit my crazy head noise. I walked out of the water closet, past the door of the church, climbed into my car and left the meeting. My emotions ran the gamut on my long ride home. Flight or fear, we've all heard of it, but have you ever been consumed by it? Anger, failure, insecurity, uncertainty, and defeat were all top of my mind and I didn't know what to do and I didn't have many choices of people to call.

It was cold that night. The payphone outside of Denny's had moisture on it and my breath was visible as I waited for Samantha's callback.

Ring, ring… "Sam?" I answered.

"Steven, are you okay?" she responded quickly.

25

"Yup, but I need to talk to someone I can trust and I'm not sure if that's you or not. But you're all I have."

"You can trust me, Steven. What did you do? What happened?"

"I guess we're about to find out, Sam. Can you meet me at location three in thirty minutes?" I asked.

"See you in thirty, Steven," she said as she hung up the phone.

Location No. 3

A shopping mall in the Valley with an adjacent multi-level parking structure which provided great cover from air surveillance. Multiple entrances/exits on both the south and north sides of the parking structure were complemented by foot escape routes inside the mall: stairs, elevators, escalators in all directions, multiple stores, buildings, and restaurants. It was a surveillance team's worst nightmare. Samantha showed up early as expected. I observed her first as she pulled into the underground parking structure. She appeared to be off her game that night. Disheveled, I would even say. Her left Vans shoe was untied, black hoodie and jeans. Her gait was quicker than I remembered as she looked surprisingly noticeably from side to side. But she appeared to be alone, which was the most important thing to me. I tracked her like a lion stalks their prey as she walked to the designated meeting area. I waited a few minutes and observed her before my approach, still nervous about my decision to contact her. We made eye contact as she lowered her purse to the ground, giving me the signal it was okay to approach. I place both of my hands in my pockets as I continued my walk towards her, reciprocating the go sign.

26

She embraced me. "Steven, are you okay?" Her smell lingered, but it was different from what I'd remembered.

"Yeah, I'm good."

"What's up? BJ's?"

"Sounds good," I said.

"Wow, it must really be bad if you didn't make a wise crack at that."

I remained silent as we walk towards BJ's. "Can you order me a beer? I need to go to the bathroom," I told her when we got there.

"Steven, you know this lay out. No need for op sec right now." Sam shook her head as the bartender took her order.

"Sam, sometimes a duck is really just a duck," I said as I headed to the bathroom checking my exits as Sam had suspected.

"So how many new boy toys are you training these days?" I asked her when I rejoined her at the bar.

"Boy toys, huh? I like that! That's a new one. So, you consider yourself my boy toy, Steven?" she asked as she took a drink of her Vodka martini, dirty of course.

I didn't respond right away, waiting to see if she was willing to break the rules and answer my question.

"I guess I have a girl toy then, but no new boy toys," Sam answered as she looked me in the eye, knowing that I would be looking for any nonverbal clues of deception.

"Wow, a girl, huh? Animal rights groups are that bad right now?" I asked her, fishing to see how much she was willing to trust me.

"Nice try, Steven. You know I can't tell you her assignment. Are you done with your tests?" she said as she stared at the large fish tank

27

located on the back wall of the bar. "Hey what kind of fish would you be if you could be any fish in the world?"

"What are you talking about?"

"Seriously, what kind of fish would you be if you could be any fish in the world," she asked me again. "I think I would be a whale. They're the kings of the ocean and no one really messes with them except the damn Asians."

"A whale is not a fish. It's a mammal, Sam." I couldn't help but correct her.

Sam laughed out loud as she finished her drink. "That's why you're too smart for this job, Steven."

"You think I'm too smart for this job because I know that a whale is a mammal and not a fish?"

"Exactly! Bartender, could I get another round and an old fashioned for my friend here," Sam asked the bartender. "Now, Steven, have you decided if you're going to tell me what you did yet?"

I passed on my beer and took a sip of the old-fashioned Sam had ordered for me. The bourbon shocked my tongue and slightly warmed my throat as I swallowed it, causing me to choke slightly. "What I'm going to tell you is just between you and me, okay?"

Sam didn't respond.

"I had an important meeting tonight…" I paused, but Sam didn't say anything or agree to my plea. "I don't know what happened to me, Sam, but I just flipped out. I felt like they *made* me from the beginning. Sam, this hillbilly guy knew my name and stepped into my path with a gun…"

"Stop," Sam interrupted me, but I continued to try and tell her my story.

"Steven. I said stop," she scolded me like a mother disciplining her teenager. "I don't want to know that shit, Steven. I can't know that shit, Steven. Damn it! They ask me this shit on my polygraph to keep my clearance, Steven! Shut up. And they're going to ask you too, so shut the fuck up. First of all, there is no such thing as *just between me and you in our job*. Ever. Remember that. So, you left early from the meeting and that's it? Jesus Christ," she said, obviously upset.

I nodded.

"So I'm assuming you didn't check in yet with Al or call anyone else? Right?" Sam asked.

"Nope," I said, taking a larger sip of my old fashioned. "Sam, I flipped out and left the meeting early. Al is going to kill me and kick me out of the program."

"Stop! I got it." Sam paused, finishing the rest of her drink in one gulp. "Check in with Al and go home, Steven." She signaled the bartender with her right hand, pretending to sign an imaginary check, and the bartender nodded in acknowledgement.

"You got the check, Steven. I'm out of here." As Sam got up to leave, I grabbed her by her right arm. She looked down at me in dismay, staring at my hand grasping her arm, her eyes telling me everything I needed to know as I let go. "You're fine, Steven. Al's gonna be pissed, but he's not going to kick you out. Sure, we're going to hear about it and he's gonna bitch, but your assignment is too important to the Chief and he doesn't have anyone else. Trust me. That self-serving son of a bitch needs you. You're fine," she said as she got up, instinctually readjusting her gun hidden underneath her hoodie.

"You're sure?" I asked again, not liking her advice.

"Yup."

"Why are you pissed?" I asked.

"You're too fucking nice, too clean and too smart for this bullshit. I knew it. I tried to tell you months ago this wasn't a game. Tonight, it got real for you. It's gonna get worse, sweetheart. It's gonna get worse," she said, looking through me, similar to what cops refer to as the thousand-mile stare common with someone who's *dusted.*

"You decide: just do your time like the rest of the *birds.* Stay out of trouble. Give them a little bit of info from time to time and that's it. No one will know but you," she said as we hugged, whispering in my ear, "I wasn't here. You hear me? Don't fuck me, Steven." She kissed me on my cheek and left.

Sitting there at the bar, sipping my old fashioned, I reached into my pocket and pulled out the silver dollar my father gave me secreted in my wallet. A 1903, Susan B. Anthony silver dollar. Rubbing it, flipping it, staring at it. A lifetime of my dad's lessons hit me like a freight train with each flip of the coin. My dad was my hero and one of my best friends. A confidante to this day. Growing up, I thought my dad could whoop Superman's ass, was smarter than Einstein himself, and could beat Carl Lewis in a race. It seemed there was nothing that my old man couldn't do or didn't know. Strong as an oak tree, worked harder than any man I know, wise. He could build or fix anything unless it was plumbing. The MacGregor kryptonite. Provided for his family and taught me the value of hard work, education, manhood, family, and patriotism. A no excuse, no quit approach, all built with little formal education.

My father's gift of a simple coin served a purpose I'm certain he fortuitously knew would come. A reminder that he was with me. A reminder that I was a MacGregor. A reminder of what MacGregor's stood for. Clarity came to my mind. Not about Al or the meeting. Acceptance. Acceptance of my situation. I knew what had to be done.

Sam was right. I checked in with Al later that night and he was pissed, but he didn't kick me out of the program. He just seemed tired and wanted to get off the phone. It was a non-event except in my head.

Location No. 4

A few days later, I received an unexpected page. Beep, beep, beep... *940-4220*. Interesting, I thought. 940? Why was Jay wanting me to meet with him? It wasn't quarterly training. Location number four at 2:20. It was random, but I was pleased to see that I would be meeting with Jay and not the usual crowd.

Location number four: Chinatown corridor near a hotel where I used to meet SAU for training from time to time. There was a small park on the west side of the hotel with a koi pond, park benches and a grassy area where you would often see several older Asians practicing tai chi. Jay liked this place because it didn't have the normal dog pee aroma or sleestaks walking around talking to themselves.

I arrived at the location early just as I was trained, going through my op-sec protocols. I didn't see Jay sitting at the park bench where we were supposed to meet but there was another man sitting in our spot. I circled the park a few times but I still didn't see Jay and I hadn't received any other communication that the meeting had been changed or canceled. Confused, looking at my watch to see if I had reached the crucial thirty-minute mark, which was an automatic scrub of the meeting followed by assistance protocols: 242 hours. *Jay, you have eight minutes. Where the heck are you? I hope you're okay*, I thought to myself as I walked over to the bench.

"Hi, do you mind if I sit here?" I asked the man sitting on the bench. He turned his head briefly but didn't' answer me. The man, dark brown hair, freshly shaved with a slight hint of Old Spice aftershave, walking cane resting on his left side with a fritz handle, dark sunglasses, dressed in a button down red and black checker Pendleton shirt, blue jeans with black boots.

"You're late, 03," the man said, to me referring to my undercover call sign.

"Jay, what the heck?" I said, shocked. "What are you doing? You shaved your beard!"

Jay took his glasses off as he broke out in a chuckle which was the extent of any type of laughter you will get out of Jay.

"Pretty good, huh! I think my old lady is going to go crazy for my new look, don't you?" Jay said.

"Yup, I would do you if I was gay, Jay. Looking pretty good, sir," I said, still in shock that his old Santa Claus look had been replaced with a bad impression of Antonio Banderas.

"Yeah, I heard this militia movement is heating up, so I thought I'd go back under the sheets with you, my friend," he said as he looked at me.

"Really? Okay," I said.

32

"Naaaa, I'm just fucking with you. My old lady would kill me but I am dressed like John Travolta to show you a few things." Jay

"You think you look like John Travolta?" I asked him.

"Absolutely. You don't?"

"Ahh, no. Not at all, Jay. I'm not seeing it, sir."

"That's what my wife said! I don't have much time. I have a meeting in an hour. So how the fuck are you, bud?"

I knew *meeting* was code for a tee time at the Montebello club.

"I'm good, Jay, thanks."

"Great, here is your mail and I also need you to look over your credit union statement and initial the bottom just to prove that we're not stealing your pitiful police salary." Jay laughed.

"Will do, Jay," I said as Jay got up to leave me alone, respecting my privacy as I went through my mail.

The mail stack was light on this visit so I went through it quickly without shedding any tears. I was looking for Jay but I couldn't find him again. After several minutes, I saw him in the second row of Asians practicing tai chi in the park. *This guy is something else*, I thought to myself as Jay broke the ranks and walked towards me.

"Ahh, I love that shit. Have you ever tried it before?" Jay asked.

"No sir. It looks very boring to me. Besides, I'm not an old Asian dude," I said, showing my ignorance.

"Exactly. You definitely have to love yourself to practice it correctly. You would be surprised what you find out about yourself. Most people don't like what they see, so they quit," he said with a chuckle, shaking his head.

"So, Sam said you shit the bed at your last militia meeting and you called her? What the fuck happened?"

Speechless, I didn't respond right away.

"What, you thought she wasn't going to tell anyone and that you could trust her, right?" Jay said with another chuckle. "Are we clear on that lesson?"

"Crystal," I said, referencing a Tom Cruise movie line. "I think that's a bit of an exaggeration. Okay, maybe not." I was still in disbelief that Sam had told him. "I was honestly fine, then I don't know what happened. I felt like everyone was watching me and they knew that I was a cop. I became hypersensitive to everything, man. It was crazy; my heart began to race, my legs got heavy like I couldn't even walk, Jay. It was bizarre," I said.

Jay interrupted me, "Look at these ducks in the pond. What do you see?"

"Hmmm. I don't know. I see two ducks swimming in a pond," I said, wondering if Jay had Alzheimer's.

"Just watch them for a minute and I'll be back. That tai chi stuff makes me want to pee," he said.

Strange, but that was Jay. I half studied the ducks just because they were cool. There were two ducks, a male and a female, floating in the pond and a third duck, a smaller female standing on the perimeter. The third duck would enter the pond and immediately the other two ducks would paddle towards and begin quacking at the third duck, causing her to hop out of the water. The third duck would then wait for the other two ducks to paddle away and try to enter the pond again. The two ducks would quickly paddle over and run the third duck out of the pond. I watched this repeat itself over the next ten minutes until Jay returned.

"Do you have it figured out?" Jay asked.

"I do," I said with confidence.

"Great. Who's in charge?" Jay asked.

"The male duck of the pair is the one leading the charge," I said.

"Do you think he's scared?"

"No."

"Look again at his feet paddling under the water then look at the female's."

The male duck's feet were going a hundred miles an hour but surprisingly the female's were noticeably slower.

"You see, I'm not a duck but I would argue the male duck has just as much anxiety as the third duck he is running off, but the female duck has the least amount of anxiety because she feels safe by the side of the male duck. There's safety in numbers and more anxiety when you're alone trying to enter a group."

"Oh, wow. You're right. I didn't see that," I said in amazement.

"So, apply this to what we do. In the beginning, it doesn't matter which duck you are. The one joining the group or the one in the charge, you'll both have anxiety and both of your little feet will be paddling like hell under water. It's normal and it goes both ways. Remember there's safety in numbers, but which duck are you striving to be and how do you get there?"

"Are you telling me I need to dress up like a female duck, Jay?" I asked.

"Whatever it takes, bud, but do you get my point? Get next to someone that will vouch for you and let them run off your naysayers. Safety in numbers. They'll take on the point and you just go along for the ride paddling slowly. Be the bitch," Jay said with another chuckle. "Now, next level stuff here. I want you to look again at the pond but watch the koi. You do know what a koi is, don't you?"

"I actually do. We had a koi fish pond growing up. It was my dad's pride and joy and I used to hate to clean that dang pond," I said as I reminisced. I watched as the koi swam lazily around the pond for several minutes, then it happened. One of the Kikusui koi came up from the bottom and nipped at the male duck's feet. The two ducks panicked, splashing as they lunged forward to the other side of the pond.

"Wow... I got it. But I didn't even really see the koi in the beginning!" I said.

"We can learn everything from the animal world. You said it. You didn't even see the koi in the beginning but they were in the game the whole time observing, gathering intel, and then they changed the entire dynamic. What's cool about it, no one, including the ducks, didn't even know they had that kind of power or influence. Find a way in your new world to be the koi," Jay explained as I nodded, processing what Jay was saying and immediately trying to figure out which role the koi played in domestic terrorism.

KLC Militia

Approximately one week later. A Tuesday about 2 PM. Tuesdays were my days off and the mailman Luis always delivered the mail at 2 PM. Give or take a few minutes. There was a June gloom feel in the air, but it wasn't June and Luis handed me my mail which included a few bills and a large manilla envelope addressed to me, but it didn't have a return address. Inside was a typed welcome letter to the KLC militia's newest member. My heart began to race as I continued to read the welcome letter. I remember starting over and reading it again because I'd always been a slow reader. Also inside was a militia identification card (laminated 2x3 inch card, yellow in color). The front of the identification card read:

King Louden County Militia
Private Steven Mathews
Serial #10063

The back of the identification card had the militia pledge that I remembered them saying during the meeting just after the Pledge of Allegiance. Also included was a booklet that included the KLC militia mission statement, operational protocols, and code of conduct for militia members. It looked so formal and organized; it caught me off guard. Then it hit me. I'm in a militia! I was so excited! It was like I'd just received news that I'd been accepted into Harvard – well, not really, but you get my point. Who could I call? Well, I guessed I couldn't tell anyone but Al or Claire and it was Al's week on call.

I figured I would kill two birds with one stone since I was hungry so I ran down to the Denny's. Slightly out of breath when I arrived, I paged Al, code one. Twenty minutes ticked by and he still hadn't returned my call. Starving, I saw Maria walk by inside and caught her eye. Recognizing me, she waved. Still starving, I mouthed, "Can I order my usual please?"

She nodded. Excited, I paged Al a second time, changing my page to code two.

Waiting outside for Al's call, I still couldn't believe that I was in a militia as a cop! How crazy was that? I'd done it. I remember feeling so proud until Maria's knock on the window pointing to my food brought me back to reality. Giving up on Al for the time being, I went inside and wolfed down my Yankee pot roast with mashed potatoes. I never heard from Al that night; there was a mix up with who was on call that week. Not very comforting considering it was my lifeline.

Several days later: *ring, ring, ring... Oh my gosh, what time is it*, I thought, fumbling to see my alarm clock. "Hello?" I answered.

"Hey, Steven, It's your Commander. Were you sleeping?" a man's voice inquired.

My brain immediately starting trying to remember my commander's name, knowing that this couldn't be a good phone call, but his voice was chipper. Then it hit me. This was my militia commander and not my police commander.

"Paul?" I asked.

"Hey, Steven, looks like I caught you sleeping again," He said.

"What time is it?" I asked.

"Ahh…12:35. Wow, it's later than I thought. Sorry, Steven," Paul said.

"Can you not call me this late please unless it's an emergency. I have to work in the morning. What's up?" I said, obviously perturbed because I valued my sleep.

"Yeah, sorry about that. I'll do my best. Just checking to make sure that you received your ID and your packet in the mail?"

"Yeah, I did. That's why you called me at 12:35?" I asked.

"Well, that was one reason, but the main reason is to let you know that KLC has expanded and we want you to start attending the Denali Park Unit in the Valley so you don't have to drive up to Bakersfield anymore. They're a different unit under KLC but they're in Los Angeles near you."

"Okay, thanks, Paul. Is that it?"

"That's it, do you want to write down your new captain's name?"

"Ummm, right now? Uh, yeah sure. Give me a second, I have to find something to write with." I got out of bed to retrieve something to write with.

"Sorry again, Steven. His name is Captain J and his phone number is 818-626-3214. Call him in the morning if you can, I think they have a meeting tomorrow night and they want you to attend."

"Okay, will do, Paul," I said, just trying to get off the phone wanting to go back to sleep.

"Great! Death to the New World Order, Steven," Paul said as he hung up the phone.

Debrief

The next morning, I checked in with Claire and told her about my wake-up call with Paul and that they wanted me to attend a militia meeting in the Valley.

"Steven, are you sure that he said the meeting was tonight in the Valley?"

"Yes, I believe so, but I was half asleep," I said.

39

"Steven, I need you to be sure because this would be huge. We don't know about any militia units operating in Los Angeles and the Chief will go ballistic." Claire's voice quivered.

"I'm just telling you what he told me. But the phone number he gave me has an 818-area code so it fits. All I know is his name is Captain J. I don't know if that's the letter *J* or like the bird," I said.

"You didn't get a last name or an address?"

"No, I didn't, ma'am," I said.

"Why didn't you ask for a last name?"

"I'm not going to ask for his last name, ma'am," I said respectfully.

"Yeah, you're right. Sorry, Steven. I just know that the brass are going to ask me a ton of questions that I don't know the answers to."

"Ma'am, let me go back to my place and call this guy from my phone and see what he's about, then I'll call you back," I said.

"Okay, sounds good. Call me when you know something."

8:32 AM

Dang it. I have to be at work by 9 AM, I thought to myself as I rushed back to my apartment to call Captain J. If cell phones had only existed back then things would have been much easier; however, I stuck to my security protocols and called Captain J from my home phone.

"This is J," a deep voice answered.

"Hey J, this is Steven. Paul gave me your number and told me to call you this morning," I said.

"Steven who?"

"Steven Mathews. Paul told me to call you," I said.

40

"Hey Steven, Paul who?"

"Umm, I don't know Paul's last name but he's my Commander with the KLC militia," I said.

"Hey Steven, we don't say the M word here because we never know who is listening," J said.

"Okay, sorry about that. I never heard of that before," I said.

"Paul told me a little about you and thought that you might be a good fit for our club here in the Valley. Would you like to attend a meeting and see if you like our group?" J said.

"Sure, I'd like to check it out," I said.

"Great. We're meeting tonight at my house in the Valley at 7. Can you make it?"

"Yeah, I can make it," I said.

"Great. My address is 1663 Saticoy. See you then." J hung up the phone.

8:47 AM

I got ready to go to work and drove back to the CVS pay phones to call Claire back.

"Hey Steven," Claire answered the phone quickly. "Let me guess. He didn't answer or the phone number is BO."

"No, he answered. I'm going to the meeting tonight at 7 at his house. His address is 1663 Saticoy in the Valley," I said.

"Seriously?" Claire asked with surprise.

"Hey Claire. That's all I know but I got to go. I'm already late for work, ma'am," I said, looking at my watch.

41

"Steven. I need you to hang out for a second while I make a call. Sorry, but I'll call you right back," she said as I looked at my watch: 8:59 AM.

Standing next to the bank of pay phones: 9:10, 9:25, 9:45.

Ring, ring... "Hey Claire," I quickly answered.

"Sorry it took so long. I need you to meet me at 1300 downtown at our normal location to debrief this," Claire said.

"Claire, I have to work today and I'm already really late. What are we going to debrief at 1?"

"Sorry, I know, but can you do it please?" Claire asked nicely in her motherly voice. You would never suspect Claire of being a cop. She seemed more suited for a kindergarten teacher and didn't have a mean bone in her body. Frustrated, I agreed and called in sick to work, losing that day's pay.

1 PM

I arrived early as always to complete my op sec. It was another Denny's restaurant. Claire gives me the all-clear sign so I began to approach. She was sitting with Al which made me chuckle inside because they looked like the odd couple. Al was consumed in the morning paper as always, not even acknowledging me as I sat down.

"Well, you caused quite a stir on the 6th floor, Junior," he said.

"Why? What's going on?" I asked, puzzled.

"Well, we checked with all of our analysis and the FBI domestic terrorism task force on militias and they all tell us that there aren't any militias in Los Angeles. Now you're telling us that you're going to a militia meeting tonight at 7. Get it?"

"Okay. Cool. The guy sounded normal to me," I said.

"What does normal sound like?" Al asked, lowering his newspaper as we made contact, always the contrarian.

"I don't know. He just sounded like the other guys. A little paranoid, but normal, I guess."

"Okay, we did a work up on the location and the phone number and we're scrambling a surveillance unit over to the address as we speak to see what we can find out," Claire said as she slid a manilla folder across the table for me to review just like you see in the movies.

I opened the folder. A small wallet-sized photo was paperclipped to what looked like a rap sheet. The appearance of the man in the photo didn't match what I had imagined "J" would look like in my mind. My mind immediately rewound to a blind date I'd once had before I met Liz. It was common for my friends, friend's girlfriends, co-workers, even the mailman, to set me up on blind dates. I was always the single guy. Her name was Irene and she worked as a school teacher with my buddy's girlfriend. I of course said why not and we spoke on the phone for a few days before we decided to meet for coffee, which ironically, I still hadn't acquired a taste for.

Irene's voice would best be described as chipper, flowing and confident. I imagined her as fairly attractive, medium build, shoulder-length blonde hair signifying conservatism or safety, with great teeth. Soft skin, maybe a little pale, with her feet on the smaller side since I knew she was not an athlete. She was very well spoken with high energy, and talkative, which typically meant she would lose a few points on the

43

attractive scale. When we met in person my perception was completely off; she had very short brown hair, almost a *bob*, which was an immediate deal killer for me. Her teeth were straight, but I noticed a tinge of yellow, and her energy was much more mellow in person and we struggled to keep the conversation going. Strange to say the least. Anyway. Not to digress here but when I saw the picture of "J" it struck me in a similar way.

"Steven, did you hear what I said?" asked Al.

"Ah, yes I did, sir. Sorry about that, but he looks familiar to me," I said.

"Really? From Drew's life or Steven's?" Claire asked.

"Not Drew's life. I think he's one of the guys that stopped me at that first KLC meeting. But I'm not certain," I said.

"Really?" Claire asked me.

"Yeah. Here, take this back. I don't want to know anything about this guy," I said, closing the folder and sliding it back across the table.

"What do you mean?" Al asked me.

"It will mess me up. I don't want to see it and I don't want to know anything about this guy. Just take a look at his file and if you think there's anything dangerous that I need to know then just tell me," I asked.

"Are you sure?" Claire asked, turning her head towards Al. "All *birds* that I have dealt with always look at the work ups on targets. Al, is he required to look at the files?"

"No, he doesn't have to if he doesn't want to. His call I guess," Al said as he went back to reading the newspaper.

"Steven, are you good? Do you need anything from us?" Claire asked, her mother instincts kicking in.

"No, I'm good for now, but thank you," I said.

"Okay, are you sure?"

"No. I promise I'm good. Is that it?"

"Yup, you can stay and eat if you like?" Al said.

"That's all you needed or wanted to debrief me on?" I asked.

"Yes, that's it for now. But make sure you check in with Claire after your meeting. She's got the on-call this week," Al continued, still reading the newspaper.

"Will do. I thought there was more to this debrief. We could have covered that on the phone couldn't we?" I asked.

"Well, I guess we could have but the Lieutenant wanted to make sure that you saw his file before the meeting," Claire said.

"The Lieutenant? Why is the Lieutenant involved in this?" I asked.

Al broke out with a chuckle, lowering the newspaper. "Ahh, naiveté. Do you remember Claire, when you used to have that back when you started the job?"

Claire respectfully nodded her head.

Denali Park Militia

A modest house located in the Valley on a busy street. Cars lined up and down the curbside making it difficult to find parking. I made a few passes looking at the cars to see if I could gather any intel. There was a small Toyota pickup truck that had a bumper sticker: *Don't Mess with The Second* with an image of a rifle. That had to be the vehicle of a militia member, I thought. *Six marys have thirty-seven kids and the youngest is nineteen. Six marys have thirty-seven kids and the youngest is nineteen* (6M03719).

It was dark when I walked up to the house, but the lawn appeared to be kept and watered. Block walls separating the neighbors, with wood fences front facing with a single gate on the west side. A rather large *beware of dog* sign posted on the fence but I didn't hear a dog. The landscaping was modest: an olive tree in the front yard which I couldn't help but feel for its owner because of the mess they cause. A standard front hedge across the front window was manicured as if it had been recently cut, but the yard lacked any type of color I imagined I would say in the daylight. A steel security screen door with a camera mounted off to the right covering the walk way; a red infrared light softly shone in the darkness, alerting any welcome or unwelcome guests that the camera was functional. The standard local alarm company's sign posted on the west side. The house was otherwise dark except for a single light shining on a *Don't Tread On Me Flag* mounted to the east side of the house.

I could hear talking when I reached the door. At least three separate voices, all male, and the sound of a chain rattling which I could only assume was the watch dog.

The door opened before I knocked.

"Steven?" a man asked me, unlocking the security screen door which had two locks.

"Yes, I am. Are you J?" I asked.

"It's actually Jason, but most call me J," he responded. "Come in. I'm glad you could make it."

J was small in stature for a man, maxing out at 5'7". Medium build, 165lbs, full curly beard, with dark hair, late thirties, dressed in a brown and black flannel shirt, light brown khaki pants, cargo style, and work boots. A spider co. folding knife, black, was clipped to his left front pocket, indicating he was left-handed. His eyes were dull brown, but I didn't notice much life in his soul.

"Everyone, this is Steven, or is it Steve?" J announced to a group of five.

"It's Steven, but most call me Steve," I responded, mirroring J's answer. The group all welcomed me and stood up to introduce themselves with formal handshakes, including the "watchdog," who after a few foreplay sniffs mounted my leg.

Kevin, Ralph, John and David. David, a black man with steely eyes, surprised me. A black guy. Didn't see that one coming, but maybe the militia movement wasn't tied to the white supremacists like we'd originally thought. As I shook all of the guys' hands one by one their energy seemed within the normal range except David, the black guy's. His grasp was over the top firm, almost crushing, and when I would mirror his strength, he would grip even harder. Assuming the handshake duel had gone on long enough, I released my grip, but David continued to hold onto my now limp hand, crushing it even more and never saying a word.

"Welcome, Steven, to the Denali Park militia. A little about us: we're also part of the KLC militia but we're considered the Denali Park cell. You will no longer report to Paul or Joel out of the main core; you will report to me now and I am a Captain. Steven, you're still a private rank, correct?" J asked me.

"Yes I am," I responded.

"Great. Well, just check out a few of our meetings and if you'd like to join us just let me know and we'll transfer your paperwork over here. Let's get started. David, do you want to start us out with the Pledge of Allegiance and our oath."

"Will do, Captain," David said as he started to recite the Pledge of Allegiance followed by the militia oath. The meeting lasted about an hour and a half. The main discussion revolved around several recent sightings of *black unmarked helicopters* seen over J's house and in the downtown Los Angeles area. The helicopters were identified as military type, but lacked any official markings such as police or fire department, which concerned the group. The group believed that the government was performing illegal surveillance on militia members in the area with the mission of seizing their weapons.

"Well, shouldn't we bed down these birds to see where they're landing?" Ralph asked.

"I agree, but that's going to be difficult for us to do," Kevin said.

"Hey listen guys, let's just table this topic for the militia summit coming up. We've spent way too much time on this tonight. We'll see if the other groups are seeing these black birds. We have some administration issues we need to cover before we close in prayer. So, who's not going to this year's summit?" J asked as he looked around to the group for confirmation. "Steven, you're welcome to come with us or the main KLC group if you like?" he said.

"I'll go with you guys if that okay," I said, even though I didn't have any idea what J was referring to about the summit.

"Great, we could use the help, Steven. We're responsible for three security shifts during the event, but they haven't finalized the schedule yet. As far as gear, bring your full kit and it's most likely going to be hot. Did Paul give you all the details on the summit?"

"No, he didn't," I said.

"No problem. We're going to close in prayer and adjourn the meeting if you could stay after and I'll give you some information."

"Sure," I said.

"Okay, boys. Let's close. Father, we thank you for these brave men that have the courage to stand up to the government, to protect the Republic and our Constitution. To fight against the New World Order, to sacrifice our lives to protect what you have put in place. In your name we pray. Amen," J said and adjourned the meeting.

"J, can I use your restroom?" I asked, hoping to perform my op sec protocols for future meetings and to see what kind of intel I could gather about J.

"Yes, it's the second door on the left," he responded, motioning towards the hallway.

The hallway had a few photographs hanging on the wall. The first picture was of a much younger J with his arm around a woman, most likely his wife based on the pose. The picture had been taken in a tropical environment. Hawaii? The second photo was of a military group. Army – Ranger Class. It had a number, but I couldn't make it out as I walked by. I opened the first door on the left. Appeared to be a bedroom converted to a work space/office. The floor was cluttered, gun safe off to the left of the front window facing the street and a computer on a desk.

"Next one," J called out.

"Oh, sorry J," I said, closing the door, pointing towards the second door and looking for confirmation before I entered. J gave me the nod so I entered. A half bathroom with a large mirror covering the entire wall, a popular eighties design, with a single sink that was surprisingly clean. I lifted the toilet seat up and there were urine stains on the back side of the seat that looked like they had been there a while. Very thin toilet paper generally associated with frugal types. The trash can was empty. Flushing the toilet, I moved quickly to the cabinet underneath the sink. Toilet paper, Old Spice, bar soap, and tampons. I didn't see any hidden firearms. The small hand towel hanging next to the door had an odor, indicating it hasn't seen a washer in a while. Lack of windows, no crawl space – *where is my exit in this place*, I thought as I walked out of the bathroom.

"Come into the kitchen, Steven. Would you like something to drink?" J asked.

"No, I'm good, but thanks," I replied.

"Here is a flyer on the summit. It's down in Borrego Springs. It's supposed to be a large event I'm told. Groups from around the country are going to attend."

"Great, I'll try and get the time off from work. What do I need to bring?" I asked.

"Just try and get the time off for now and we'll focus on what to bring, the agenda, duties, all that crap over the next two meetings. In the meantime, let me get you an ID."

"Okay, sounds good. I'll see you Thursday then," I said.

As I walked out, I was trying to remember everything that I had gathered from all of the attendees: married, kids, professions, descriptions, identifiers such as scars, house layout, license plates, not to mention the general topics of the meeting. It was daunting and I was mentally exhausted. My standard protocol after I left a meeting was to page my handler my call sign (03) – then a code four which meant all was good. It would look like this: 503-4444; however, in this case I wanted him to call me back so I punched in 503-2222, followed by the pay phone number.

50

9:02 PM

Ring, ring, ring…

"Hey Al, thanks for calling me back," I said.

"What's up kid. Everything okay?" he enquired.

"Yeah, all good here. Hey, can we debrief tonight because I got some good stuff and I have to work in the morning," I asked.

"That's why you called me?"

"Yeah, I just don't want to forget it and I can't keep missing work," I pleaded.

"No, let's just do it in the morning before you go to work. I'll meet you at 0600 at the Denny's. Great job," Al said as he hung up the phone.

Frustrated, I hung up, worried that I was going to forget half of the intel that I had just gathered. I didn't sleep much that night; my mind was preoccupied with just making it to 0600 hours without a memory dump or oversleeping just like my college days.

Debrief

The next morning Al and I met at the Denny's in downtown Los Angeles near the jail and I gave him an overview of the meeting. His reaction was disbelief. He couldn't believe that there was an actual active militia in the city and that there was an upcoming militia summit being held near San Diego which wasn't that far from Los Angeles. I remember his reaction caught me off guard. I thought he would be elated at the information I was giving him, but he wasn't. He wasn't excited; he almost seemed bothered by it.

"I need to write this stuff down," he said, fumbling with his newspaper searching for what I assumed was a pad and pen.

"I'll be right back. Can you order my food for me? I left my notepad in the car and I'll be right back," Al said as he got up to go to his car which was parked right in front of the Denny's in violation of op-sec protocols. I could see Al tossing his car like me and Rivas used to do with gangsters' cars looking for drugs or guns. After a few minutes, Al slammed his car door and walked back towards the restaurant empty-handed.

"Steven, let's go over everything one more time and then I'll get you out of here so you can get to work on time," he said with a slight tone of concern.

Frustrated with Al as always, I start from the beginning again and regurgitated everything over the next hour including license plates, names, descriptions, professions, member philosophies. It was mentally exhausting to stay that on top of my game and it took forever.

Later that day, I received a page at work: 930-3333. A code three page from Al. I'd never received a code three page before; cops' brains are naturally programmed to start with the worse-case scenario during emergency times especially when there is a lack of information. My mind immediately thought something had happened to my mother. My heart raced uncontrollably and I quickened my pace to get back to my work space where I could use the phone.

"Hey, do you have more of the Coolio albums on sale?" a man – and I am using this term lightly here – yelled at me.

"What?" I responded, not understanding what he was asking me.

"Coolio. Yo! Do you have *mo* of the Coolio albums on sale?" he asked me again, obviously upset.

"Ah, yes. I believe we do in the back, but I'm helping someone right now and I'll be right with you," I said and continued to walk towards the phone.

"You, ain't helpin' no one, you cracker motherfucker," the man said, catching me off guard with the *cracker* reference. I started to chuckle. I had been called a few names based on my race before, but never *a cracker motherfucker*. Is that even a thing, I thought? But, genius nevertheless. The man strolled towards me with his head cocked to the side just slightly, his chin pointed upward, his chest puffed out and his fists clasped by his side.

"Yo, his name is Whocco. Not cracker motherfucker – and he's with me," I heard, recognizing Oz's voice. I saw him walking towards us with his gangster stroll on full display. His right and left hand quickly met just north of his right hip during his stroll. His fingers contorted in a way that mine just didn't have the coordination or flexibility to perform, flashing his clique's gang sign quickly at the man.

"Go about your business, Whocco. I got this foo," Oz said, always leaving the letter *L* off of the word *fool* when he was in gangster mode.

I took his advice. I wasn't familiar with that type of customer service training and it didn't look like it was going to end well, so I proceeded to the phone.

"Al. What happened?" I asked.

"What do you mean what happened?" Al responded.

"Well, you paged me with 3333's so I thought something happened." Explaining the obvious.

53

"No. Nothing happened, but the Captain wants me to meet with you right now and get last night's meeting info documented on an intel report," Al said.

"You paged me with 3333's to meet with you to debrief a third time?" I asked.

"Yes. We can meet wherever you want," Al said, somewhat apologetic.

"Al, I can't meet you right now. I don't want to leave work early for a debrief that we've already done twice. I get off at 5:30 and we can meet, but I have that meeting at 7 tonight."

"I know. But the Captain wants it done now because he has to brief the Chief that there's an active militia in the city. Wait, what meeting do you have tonight?" Al asked.

"I have the guy that's speaking at the Granada Forum in the Valley. That's at 7, but I can be a little late if I have to," I said.

Granada Forum

On Sundays it was a pop-up church, but during the week it could be best described as a grass roots location for all different types of forums. There were speakers for animal rights, anti-police, homeless, abortion, domestic abuse, etc. You name it, it was on the calendar at the Granada Forum. Tonight, the featured speaker was speaking about the influx of illegal Mexicans coming across the border. The militia believed that our government was purposefully allowing illegal immigrants to come across to suck the American economy dry, all part of the New World Order's plan for a one world government and the abolishment of the United States Constitution.

I arrived at the Granada Forum thirty minutes late after debriefing with Al again. My stomach was rumbling but not due to nerves; I was starving. The speaker, Larry Nelson, a pudgy older white dude dressed in biker boots and blue jeans with a silver chain attached to his right belt loop disappearing into his back right pocket, white tee shirt with a black biker vest. His biker vest was decorated nicely, similar to most command staffs' office wall, which I always referred to as their *I love me wall.* Military related patches randomly placed throughout his vest, similar to an abstract painting nicely pieced together. The military has a saying that I heard over and over throughout my training in my later years: KISS (Keep It Simple, Stupid), but man they sure didn't follow their own advice at times with all of their patches, ribbons, ranks, and medals. My initial impression was that this was going to be a shit show and I wanted to leave, but I decided to give it a chance. I was mostly curious about how this *militia movement* was so far-reaching unlike other movements I had studied. There was a white supremacist element on the surface of the movement, yet there were black guys involved, second amendment loyalist, extreme patriots, women, and now bikers? The crossover was impressive but more intriguing to me was how it had successfully cross-pollinated across multiple platforms.

Larry spoke for about an hour and was surprisingly captivating and very knowledgeable. He was pushing the H.R.560 – Immigration Reform Act of 1995. The highlights of the proposed reform act would:

1. Restrict Alien eligibility for welfare;
2. Increase border patrol funding for wages and personnel;
3. Increase funding to detect Alien documentation fraud.

The room sat about hundred people and there were not enough chairs to accommodate the audience, mainly all former President Bush fans still whining over the President Clinton victory a year prior. Towards the end of Larry's speech his dialogue noticeably switched tone:

"Mexicans coming across the border in droves... committing crimes, killing Americans, selling their drugs to our kids, breading our women! Mexicans sucking the American economy dry... why are we funding illegals? Send their asses back home to their own country! I asked you all that are here tonight. What are you going to do about it? This should be a call to action for you! This is your *shot heard around the world* moment. There are things you can do. Seek out your local political action groups, militias, councilman. Hell, I don't care. Just do something and Fuck the New World Order!" Larry passionately told the group and concluded his performance. The crowd stood up, erupting into applause.

The host took the mic. "Thank you, Larry. Great Stuff! Very informational. He will stick around for questions and for those of you that want to know what you can do see me," the host said as the meeting adjourned.

I walked up to the host and introduced myself to see if he had anything that might interest me as it related to militias. Next thing I knew, he introduced me to *Tom*, who ran a small patriot group just outside of the city. Tom and I walked out of the building together exchanging niceties and other anti-government small talk in the parking lot and exchanged phone numbers before parting ways. I was able to see his license plate before I walked to my car: 56810D1. *568 assholes, 10 dicks and 1 woman attended this meeting… 568 assholes, 10 dicks and 1 woman attended this meeting*, I repeated, committing his license plate to memory.

Rainier Park Patriot Group

Tom and I connected the next day via the phone and he was very elusive about himself and his patriot group. His speech was monotone, deliberate, and cautious. I struggled to connect with him on the phone and every interview/interrogation technique I used failed. Even mirroring didn't work and that always worked for me; however, I understood my interrogation tactics via the phone were not that great and I was much more successful in person. Tom and I were just not connecting, so I decided to call an audible, *The Kirsten.*

"Hey, Tom. I'm sorry, but I have to run, man. I'm sure we'll run into each other at the Forum and you have my number. Talk soon, bye," I said and hung up the phone without waiting for him to end the conversation or say goodbye.

The Kirsten – *"Confident. They need you more than you want them."* – A tactic that I'd stumbled upon early on in my dating days back in college. Joe, Shawn, and I were meeting the boys at The Barn, our favorite bar on campus, for, of course, country night. Joe parked the car in lot C and we saw three bogeys exiting a vehicle about thirty yards in front of us. I immediately had target lock on the only blonde. White cowboy hat with long flowing hair stopping in the middle of her back; red halter top, with a jean mini skirt. Legs that looked like they went on forever meeting their match, red cowgirl boots. Wow. I had no idea what she looked like from the front, but from the back she was definitely my type of woman and I was destined to meet her.

The primal instinct in me yelled out, "Hey! Wait up!"

The three girls stopped, looking back as if to say who the heck is yelling at us and that was my cue. I jogged up to the ladies, Shawn and Joe still frozen in their boots back by our car.

"Hey. Do I know you?!" my blonde girl asked me as I approached.

"Not yet. I'm Mac, your boyfriend for the night. Nice to meet you. And you are?" I said.

"Oh… Wow… Hi. I'm Kirsten," she said, introducing herself and her friends, and extending her hand for a handshake. "So, you're my boyfriend for the night?" Kirsten said with a nervous laugh, seemingly shocked by my statement yet semi-entertained.

"Yes, ma'am. Don't worry. There'll be a chance for you later to extend your girlfriend status; but only if you make probation," I said, choosing to hold her hand instead of the formal handshake she'd offered. She looked down at my hand now holding hers, not knowing if this was really cool, creepy, or if she should call the police.

"Did you say that I'm on probation?" Kirsten asked, continuing to laugh but this time looking into my eyes and trying to decide if I was worthy of a shot or not like most girls do, holding all the power.

"Of-course you are! The position just opened up and there are a lot of girls that are applying, but I'm offering you a front of the line pass," I said with a wink, adjusting my grasp on her hand as we started to walk towards The Barn and I felt a slight power shift in my favor.

"Oh wow. Who are you?" Kirsten said, again turning her head sideways looking at her girlfriends for approval, still trying to process our conversation and me holding her hand in stride.

"Mac. Your boyfriend for the night. But, remember it's just for the night unless you pass probation," I said.

"Oh. Really... And how will I know if I pass probation?" Kirsten asked, further shifting the power to me and I knew I had her.

"Don't worry, I'll let you know at the end of the night. But I like your chances so far," I said, giving her a little bit of power back.

"Well, if you're my boyfriend then are you going to buy us a drink?" Kirsten asked.

"Agreed! It's official. We just started our six-hour relationship," I said, as I felt Kirsten's hand engage, now equally grasping mine. That was it. Game over.

The power now shifted to me. Kirsten and I had a great time that night and we actually saw each other several times after that night. But I did realize something in that moment that I have used throughout my life. Confidence is everything and it can be used to transfer power, even when you don't have any. Kirsten held all of the cards and the power when she got out of the car. Kirsten didn't know that I had never approached a girl that confidently before. That I weighed 98lbs my senior year in high school. My baby face, however cute it was, always landed me in the *little brother club* with the ladies. Kirsten didn't know that I was literally pooping my pants inside, fear of rejection and embarrassment in front of my boys and that I didn't hold any of the cards. She didn't know that I thought she was way out of my league. But that night, I just didn't care and it worked. Kirsten was intrigued by my confidence and the unknown I

59

offered. She later told me that she went out with me because she just had to know. I asked her, "Know what?"

Kirsten took a long pause before she said, "I'm not sure, but it just seemed that you were so confident that I needed you more than you wanted me. I had to know why." The *Kirsten play* was born. A play that I relied on throughout my undercover days and in my professional life.

The Kirsten play worked. Tom from the Rainier Park patriot group called me back the next day and he was much more talkative, inviting me to their next meeting scheduled for the following Thursday. I agreed, but there was only one problem. I had already committed to attend the Denali Park militia meeting on the same day, a growing problem that I wasn't sure how to navigate. Tom went on to tell me that he was part of a militia in Northern California, but recently moved down to Southern California where he was in the beginning stages of starting his own patriot group. Currently, he had four members that he'd met at the Granada Forum and they had been meeting once a week for the past three months. I could tell that Tom didn't have much experience in a leadership role, my guess was he lacked military experience based on his op sec protocols, like I had originally thought. He was blinded by my existing membership in the Denali Park and KLC militia groups and offered me a second in command position with his new founded patriot group. That's right. No background checks. Not even a confirmation that I was a member of the Denali Park and KLC militia groups. It was amazing. Just as I was taught in training: *These groups want to believe that you are down for the cause and not a cop. Your job is to give them an excuse to believe it.* Once I gave Tom an excuse to validate his desires and beliefs, game over. Not only was I now the second in command of his patriot group, but Tom, a long-term senior militia member, was now my advocate.

Approximately six months under the sheets and I was suddenly a member of three different militia groups, attending meetings two to three days a week in addition to attending the Granada Forum or other militia speaking engagements that seemed to be popping up everywhere. The militia movement was on fire and the Department knew it. Al and Claire were struggling to keep up with my schedule and before I knew it Claire told me she was out during her last debrief with me.

"Steven. I just wanted you to hear it from me first, but I'm not going to be your handler anymore," she said. I was shocked because Claire was my buffer from Al.

"What do you mean?" I asked her.

"I'm too old for this stuff, Steven. I have almost thirty years on the job and no one expected you to get into any militias, more or less as many as you have in such a short period. I've been doing this for a long time and I know it's going to get way worse and I just can't do it. The late nights waiting for you to get home. I'm not sleeping. The early debriefs. The amount of documentation. My anxiety is through the roof. I'm just too stressed and that's not what you need. This is a young man's game and that's why Mick will be replacing me," she said in a defeated way.

"Okay. I'm sorry. Is Mick..."

"Yes. You met him before. I like the guy. He's fiery and motivated, but he's new to our division. I think you can trust him, Steven. His call sign is 939 and he's going to set up a meet with you. You can still call me with anything you need until they find my official replacement."

"So that's it? You're out?" I asked.

61

"Pretty much." I could tell she was struggling to tell me something. "Steven. Umm …just, slow down. You don't have to work so hard," she said.

Confused, I said, "What do you mean?"

"You don't have to go to every meeting or join every militia group you come across. If you know what I mean..." She paused again as I tried to figure out what she was telling me. "No one will know or care. Just get through the program. That's all I'm saying."

Life Under the Sheets

"Your time is limited, so don't waste it living
someone else's life."

Steve Jobs

Even a publicly educated, med school dropout like myself realized very quickly that law enforcement did not have a handle on the militia movement. It was more far-reaching than they believed or wanted to believe, I guess. The movement was disguised behind names such as Patriots, Sovereign Citizens, Constitutionalist to Second Amendment enthusiast. Even God was thrown into the militia mix with such names as Christian Crusaders amongst others. What was even more unique and interesting to me compared to other extremist groups that I had studied was the militia movement appeared to be cross-pollinating. It penetrated whites, blacks, Asians, Hispanics, Catholics, Protestants, rich, poor and was spreading like a California wild fire during the Santa Ana winds. All these groups were the same in my book, just with a slightly different spin.

The militia movement's passion, anger against our government, and the urgency to grow the movement was palpable; however, such wasn't the case with law enforcement's response. Choose from any of the alphabet soup law enforcement agencies and there wasn't any urgency to gather intelligence or threat assessments on the militia movements. Following tradition, most law enforcement agencies are reactive instead of proactive. Timothy McVeigh caused the reactive response when he detonated the car bomb in Oklahoma City. Law enforcement agencies took notice and began to look at these movements but they were behind the curve and unfortunately in scramble mode.

Call it lucky or unlucky, I'm not certain to this day. But within two months of my first contact with the KLC militia I managed to get accepted into three different militia cells and was attending meetings two to three days a week, including a Granada Forum appearance from time to time. Things picked up very quickly for me. I didn't look at my day-to-day

64

routine as crazy spy stuff that you see on today's television. It was simple, boring, and *normal* to me at the time.

The Daily

0600 Wake up. Fix a cup of hot tea with a splash of milk and one spoon of sugar just the way momma made it with a bowl of Captain Crunch cereal.
Debrief with my handlers – If I had a meeting the night before I would meet my handlers to debrief and then go straight to work.

0630 Run (3–5 miles)

0700 Read the newspaper. Yes, there were actual newspapers back then.

0830 Shower

0830–1700 Work

1700 Dinner – Ramen, cup of noodles, PBJ, spaghetti or a beef bowl from a nearby fast-food restaurant.

1900–2200 Militia meetings or reading about the movement

2000 Read or study time

2300 Bedtime

Entertainment

When I first went under the sheets, my entertainment was trying to build furniture out of cardboard boxes using duct tape. If you haven't ever done that, I challenge you to try it. After many rolls of duct tape, I was actually successful in building a nightstand, coffee table, laundry basket, and a foot stool. Going to a movie by myself on occasion, which I had once perceived as strange, was now normal and actually, I considered it a treat. Running, which I had always hated, was now my solace. I enjoyed going for long runs mainly at night. Running cures everything! I haven't found a better way to clear your brain. Detailing my car at the local coin wash. It was crazy to me that I had to leave my apartment just to wash my car. Soaking up some sun by the generally algae invested pool; not the thick slimy type; more like the green side-wall type. I would have fired the *pool guy*, for sure. But most of all, I really enjoyed going to the book store and reading for the first time in my life by choice. I would immerse myself in books about history, economics, and religion. I truly focused on educating myself and not just trying to study to pass a class.

One day I received a strange page: 210-1111. Police call signs ending with a zero are saved for supervisors, command staff, or watch commanders (lieutenant rank); in this case it was the lieutenant of my division who I hadn't spoken with or seen since my interview. I'm sure I'm like most people: when a supervisor calls me out of the blue my brain immediately goes to, "What happened now?" I hadn't committed the lieutenant's phone number to my memory so I paged Claire to get it.

"Hey Claire, thanks for calling me back. I think the LT paged me to call him back code one, but I don't know his number. Can you give me his number and do you have any idea what he's paging me about?" I asked.

"That's strange. Are you sure it's the lieutenant?" Claire asked.

"I think so... is his call sign 210?" I asked.

"Yup. Okay, here's his number and let me know what he wants please if you don't mind after you speak with him," she said.

"Of course. Talk soon," I said, hanging up the phone and dialing the LT's number.

Ring, ring, ring... "Mac? How are you, sir?" a man's voice said, breaking protocol by referring to me by my real name.

"Yes, sir. You paged me, sir?"

"I did! Hey, I know you've been working your ass off lately and I wanted you to get away for a bit. How would you like to go to Big Bear and have lunch with me?" he asked. Big Bear, located about two hours east of Los Angeles in the mountains, was known for its ski resort.

"Sir, you want to go to lunch in Big Bear? Like the ski resort Big Bear?" I said.

"Oh sorry. Yes. I have my own plane and I'll fly us there. I was thinking I can pick you up one morning and we can fly out to Big Bear, have lunch, then I'll fly you back. Just a quick little get-away. How about it, Mac?" he asked.

It seemed like such a random request and a bit over the top, but not uncharted territory me. My buddy Gary and I were out drinking one night in college at The Barn, and he'd yelled to me, "Hey Mac! I'm going to be a pilot," as he finished his beer. Yes we might have had a little too much to drink that night; but it was country night with $1 beers. What can go wrong with that...

"You're going to do what?" I asked.

"I'm going to be a pilot!" he yelled with even more enthusiasm.

"Yeah? Well, I'm going to be an astronaut then!" I yelled back.

"No, you're gonna be my stewardess, bitch," he shot back at me. "Seriously! I just decided. That's it. I'm going to be a pilot. Think about it. Pilots get chicks. Travel the world and make bank!" I could see the pride he had as if he'd just figured out his life, six beers in.

"Even as a pilot, you still couldn't get Melissa, bro. She wants nothing to do with that six head of yours, but that's cool. Do it," I said.

A year later...

"Hey, Mac! I did it. I passed my test and I'm official. I have my private pilot's license. Where are we going?" he asked me.

"Do you want to meet at The Bull 'N' Mouth to celebrate?" I asked.

"No, dumb ass. Let's fly somewhere!" he said.

"You can fly us some where right now?" I asked him, still not believing that my best buddy could legally fly a plane. He was not a book smart kind of guy if you know what I mean, but we were always each other's wing man. Now in this case, I guess I was literally his wing man.

Forty minutes later, Gary and I were boarding a red and white Cessna 152 out of Brackett Field Airport, near Mount Baldy. It was crazy to me that Gary and I could just rent a plane and go fly somewhere. He only had forty hours of flying experience if I remember correctly and I was the first person to go flying with him without an instructor. It was awesome. I remember my wife asked me years later when I told her the story if I was scared. I was never scared. Not even when we were coming in for the landing and the plane was sideways! The plane's front wheels hit the ground pretty hard, whipping the tail around, straightening the plane as we cruised down the runway coming to a stop.

"That was cool! But you need to work on your landings," I said over the mic.

Gary went on to fulfill his dreams as an airline pilot where he remains today, flying as a captain for a major commercial airliner.

Sorry for the digression, but it was a great memory. The following week I met the LT at Whiteman Airport in the Valley where we boarded his plane and next thing I knew we were wheels up headed to Big Bear. I don't remember much about the conversation except the LT's desire to one day work at the Department's air support division where he wanted to fly helicopters. I do remember, I had one heck of a chicken pot pie.

Finances

Money was scarce, actually worse than in my college days which were tough to beat. Some months it was tough to even pay rent depending on how much work I had to miss for militia events. The arrangement I had agreed to when I entered the program was that I had to live off of and pay all of my bills with Steven's wages from the department store. I was not allowed to co-mingle any of Mac's police salary. It didn't really matter because I didn't have access to Mac's funds anyway. My handlers had all of Mac's identification, ATM, credit cards, etc. and my police salary was banked into a separate savings account that I didn't have access to. A perfect storm to save money for me because I couldn't spend it even if I wanted to.

Steven brought home about $1,300 month which had to cover rent, utilities, food, entertainment, gas, etc. That didn't leave much discretionary income left over like I was accustomed to. Frequently, I literally didn't have a dime to my name until payday. I didn't have any credit cards to bail me out or get me into debt, depending on how you want to look at it. It was paycheck to paycheck like most Americans and I swore if I ever got out of this program, I would never live paycheck to paycheck again.

Over time, I learned the system. One of my go-tos was to schedule my debriefs with my handlers around meal time because they would chit the meal and the tax payers would pay. So, thank you all you tax paying citizens for my meals over the years. Even if I wasn't hungry, I would order a plate of food and take it back to my apartment for the next day's meal. Maybe that's why to this day I'm not a big fan of leftovers. I knew my family didn't have a ton of money growing up, but I never felt we went without. For the first time in my life, I felt poor even though I knew I wasn't. Don't get me wrong when I say that I didn't have any money for food, that's true, but food was always a phone call away if I was ever truly starving. It was all part of sacrificing for me and I am proud to say that in the three years that I was under the sheets, I only had to summon my handlers twice to dip into Mac's police savings account. Over time, I just adapted to being poor and having less and that was okay.

Friends

Steven didn't really have any friends that he spoke with on a regular basis. Ethically and morally, it was challenging. Any and all relations conceived under the cloak of lies Steven had built were terminal and didn't feel right. The lies continued to multiply like bunnies during spring. Occasionally, I enjoyed hanging out with the boys from work because it was simple. No emotions. They cared more about my favorite football team and had zero interest if I had any brothers or sisters. Men cared about what girl or which girl was my next conquest and not what I'd be doing for the holidays.

I enjoyed speaking with and did get to know a few of my neighbors in the apartment complex. One particular lady, a single mother named

Rochelle, lived directly across from me with her daughter, Sophia. Rochelle, about 5'4", thick black hair, curly, shoulder-length, spoke with a thick Hispanic accent. Rochelle was constantly feeding me and trying to teach me Spanish. It was here where I discovered two new loves: the first was my love for children. Sophia, just three years of age with a limited grasp of the English language, taught me a new level of patience, laughter, and the innocence of a child; my second love was for Albondigas soup. Oh my gosh, Rochelle's Albondigas was to die for. The heavenly smell of her soup would overtake the stairwell between our two apartments. Over the years, we developed a partnership I guess. Some might refer to it as a present-day barter system. She would feed me and teach me Spanish and I was her handyman and occasional babysitter if she had to go to the store or the laundry room. Sophia and I would hang out and play hide and seek from time to time. Simple, mind-numbing relationship, but functional and enjoyable to all parties I would say.

Mac's friends and family would write me letters to a PO box since my whereabouts and assignment was a mystery. JT's crew would pile my mail in a manilla envelope and bring it to every quarterly training. I always looked for the manilla envelope. In the early months, I would garner two manilla envelopes, stuffed. In the later months, I didn't need a manilla envelope at all.

The telephone was my main lifeline to Mac's world. Nobody likes to write. Especially men in their early twenties. In the beginning, I would call my family and friends consistently, but just as their efforts to write dissipated with time so did my calls. There was always one exception and that was my mother. I remember the first time it happened – yes, this happened more than once – *beep, beep, beep...* I looked down at my pager.

933-2222 was Claire, code two, priority page. I traveled down to my usual bank of payphones to call her back.

"Hey Claire, what's up?" I asked.

"Steven, when was the last time you called your mother?" she asked me with a stern motherly tone herself.

"What?" I asked, surprised by her question.

"Steven, your mother called me and she is worried about you because you haven't called her in a while. When was the last time you called your mother?"

Stunned, I said, "You're joking? My mother called you?"

"She did! She said that everything is fine and not to worry, but you haven't called her and that you need to call her ASAP."

I laughed out loud, shaking my head in disbelief. I of course agreed to call her, because I knew something the Department didn't know. No one would come between my mother and her children. Growing up, I was like most boys I believe. Closer to Mom as a boy, transitioning to Dad as a teenager, back to Mom as her protector as a man. She was the most loving, selfless person that I knew; my foundation, my rock; but she was a pit-bull disguised in sheep's clothing when it came to her kids. My mom didn't care about the city's top secret undercover program, the chief of police's rules, my handlers' promises, secret clearances, she just wanted to talk to her son and they better make it happen. I think they knew it.

Gangster Love

The cover vehicle I'd purchased under Steven's name was an absolute bucket (cop lingo for a turd of a car). Problem after problem and it just wasn't reliable so I traded it in for a smaller compact car with much better gas mileage. The first night I had my new (used) car a few of the boys from work invited me out to a party. I was a little nervous about going to the party because in reality, I was the only white guy and a little out of my element. But honestly at this point I really didn't know what my *element* was. Everyone met that night at our work parking lot after the store closing so we could head out to the party together.

Driving police caravan style, we stopped at Louie's liquor store in east Los Angeles and everyone pitched in to buy two twelve packs of beer. Soon after we left the liquor store, I felt the steering of my car begin to loosen, then heard a loud crash, sparks flew up and my car came to a screeching stop in the middle of the street.

What the hell was that? my inner voice exclaimed. The front axle of my car had literally snapped in two. I couldn't believe it. Panic quickly washed across my entire body, because I knew the area. A violent area located on the east side, crime-ridden, with two local gangs engaged in a territorial war: one Hispanic and the other Black.

What do I do now? I thought. I didn't own a cell phone, but I knew there was a payphone back at Louie's approximately two miles away. I didn't have any friends or family I could call in this life. I didn't have any credit cards, AAA, or any more cash. Did I call my handlers for this? Al would kill me. What the heck should I do?

They need to add this scenario to the training; you can't make this stuff up, I thought to myself.

I saw a car approaching me from the north stops in the middle of the street. The head lights were blinding, but I heard two sets of car doors open. *Do I run? Do I lock myself in the car? What's my story?*

"Whocco! What the fuck happened, bro?" I recognize Nester's voice.

Whocco? What the heck is a Whocco, I thought to myself.

"Yo. Your ride is fucked up," he said with a laugh.

"Whocco?" I started to smile. "What does Whocco mean?" I asked, not worrying about my car for that moment.

The boys started to chuckle, not quite reaching belly laugh status.

"That's you, bro," Oz said.

"Hmmm, okay. I guess. I'm not sure my mom would like it, but that's cool, I think," I said as I shook my head. "I was just driving. I didn't hit anything. So I'm not really sure what happened," I explained.

"Hey Nes, call that *foo* Shorty. He's got a tow truck and he can fix anything," Oz said. "You cool with that, Whocco?"

"Sure, but how much will he charge me? I don't have any cash on me," I said.

"Don't worry, we got you. Hey Oz, you strapped?" Nester asked.

"Naaa man, I don't do that shit no more, we'll be alright. I'm OG, these homies won't mess with me."

I couldn't believe it. These former and apparent *gang-bangers* in my police mindset, were helping me out. I was a cop. If they only knew! Weren't we *enemies,* just like the cops and robbers I used to play with my cousins?

I generally liked Oz. He was witty with a laissez-faire attitude about life; always dressed in the traditional Gangsta 101 dress code: plaid Pendleton shirt (top button only fastened) with a white wife-beater tank underneath, khakis secured with a belt, displaying the local gang initial on the buckle, white knee-high tube socks, with Vans. He smiled with his

74

eyes, soft spoken, quiet demeanor, slender build, but very witty and genuinely funny. Walked with a gangster stroll, his feet swung outward never leaving too far from the ground as he walked.

The crazy thing was. I knew of Oz's former gang and clique. I had witnessed first-hand the pain, fear, and havoc they had wreaked on communities. Ironically, the first rape investigation I handled was a sixteen-year-old girl named Josephina who was raped repeatedly at his clique's party after she passed out; my training officer believed she was drugged. The two suspects were from Oz's former *clique*. I couldn't help but wonder...

Oz seemed different to me, just a gut feeling I had. I knew where I stood with him even though we came from two different worlds. I strangely enough trusted him. *Shorty* arrived shortly, no pun intended here, and towed my car away just as they said he would. He even gave me a ride home!

I learned a lot about the gang culture or neighborhoods that night that I was never taught in the Police Academy. Here these bangers didn't really know me, but they accepted me and treated me like a brother. They gave every last dollar they had in their pockets for a *Whocco* that they really didn't know. For the first time, I began to understand why bangers refer to as their gangs as their *family*.

A couple days later I had thanked Oz again and asked him, "Why did you guys help me out the other night?"

Oz seemed surprised by my question. "Why wouldn't we help you out? You're our homeboy, man." He smiled as he placed a Barbie doll back on the shelf at work.

"Oz, if you haven't noticed, I'm white and I'm definitely not from around here," I said, stating the obvious.

"Yo man, you serious. You don't really get it do you?" Oz shook his head as he placed another Barbie back on the shelf and straightened the boxes.

I followed Oz down the toy aisle, intrigued by his response. "What do you mean?" I asked.

Oz shook his head again. "Look, I don't know how it works back in your corn fields or where ever you're from, but here… you were down for *Em* at the club that night. Those homies were from the east side and they were fucking with one of our neighborhood girls. What whetto is down for a neighborhood girl against our rival clique? That's how you got the name Whocco, foo! *White Loco*. We're down for you, *por vida* man," Oz said with a strong accent as he seemed to look through me with his steely eyes. I saw it for the first time, his inner gangster came out. I don't know how to articulate it on paper just like most cops fail to do in their police reports but it was there and it took me back slightly. I stared back at Oz in disbelief, trying to process what he was telling me because he was serious and I actually believed him.

"Yeah, but Oz… I didn't know any of that stuff that night," I explained.

"It don't matter, bro… you're *straight* now. Nobody will fuck with you or they'll be fucking with the west side locos. No foo wants that. Trust me! We don't play," Oz said as he took the lid off a can of playdough, took a whiff, and put it back on the shelf. "I love the smell of playdough, bro. Do you like the smell of it?" he asked me with a smile. As he offered me a whiff I saw the gangster leave his body.

I shook my head. "And you call *me* crazy," I said.

Time

Marking time with a small tally, month after month inside of a phone book like a prisoner does in a Hollywood movie. Maybe that's what inspired me to track my time under the sheets every month. I just can't remember the inspirational movie. Steven was settling into his new life nicely I thought. Sure, he or I had our moments, but by this time I had settled into work as a department supervisor and I had six people working for me. Five guys – no not like the hamburger joint that now exists – and one girl. My main duties were as one would guess: write the schedule, sales, stock shelves, clean, customer service, inventory, etc. I remember worrying that the store manager or the HR girl would catch me lying about my background or on my application and fire me. You know that feeling when you get called to the boss's office and you start running through all the things that you possibly did wrong? Times that by ten. However, time heals all and after six months I was settling in and actually received my first of several employee of the month awards. I also won Department Head of the Year during my second year. So, I knew if I couldn't cut it fighting domestic terrorists, I could always get a job at a department store.

Liz

Liz and I were doing better than I expected and we were trying to figure out what our new relationship was going to look like. I thought about her a lot and she kept me sane because it was one of few conversations that I felt were real and not based on lies. Looking back, it was harder on her, she had no real way of contacting me, didn't know where I was or what I was doing. I had all of the control which I have learned over the years is a key factor in a healthy relationship. Unbalanced control in a relationship generally works in the honeymoon years because love is blind. But when the love glazes over and is rooted, control has to be balanced and understood by both parties if the relationship is going to flourish. Liz had zero control and learned out of necessity to wait for my call. We spoke multiple times a day to multiple times a week, to a scheduled date and time every week.

Ring, ring, ring... I heard screaming or a loud screech as Liz answered the phone with excitement. "Babe? Is that you? Hi babe! How are you? I miss you so much. When can I see you?" Liz shot gunned questions at me.

"Hey babe. I'm good. That was some welcome," I chuckled and a rare smile formed across my face.

"Where are you? What are you doing? I know, I know... You can't tell me but you can't blame a girl for asking?" Liz seemed extra excited today. "Hey seriously, my sister is getting married and I'm her maid of honor. Of course! You can go right?" she asked.

"She's getting married? To who? John? I thought they broke up?" I asked.

"Of course, John. Silly. And yes they broke up, but they always break up. You know that. Can you go?" she asked again.

"That makes zero sense to me, Liz. But whatever. I have no idea if I can attend the wedding. Hopefully not," I said under my breath with a slight chuckle.

"Babe, stop it! It's important to me. I'm her maid of honor. It will be fun. John's okay," she continued.

"I know. I know. I was kidding, of course I'll go. When is it?" I asked.

"Next January. Put it on your calendar, okay? Will you be done playing 007 by then?"

"No, babe. I won't. But don't worry about it. I'll make it happen," I said with confidence.

"Babe?" she asked and I could tell her mood had changed and turned serious. I still don't know how women do this today: switch emotional gears and expect us men to understand.

"Yes, what's wrong?" I asked hesitantly.

"Do you think we're going to make it? It's only been six months and I'm having a hard time. Two more years seems like forever to me. Don't you?" Liz asked.

"I think we're doing good so far, babe. Sure, it's hard and I miss you too. But so far, I think we're handling it very well," I told her. "Don't you?"

"Yeah, you're right. We got this, babe." Her mood switched back to happy-go-lucky. Women!

"Good, that's my girl. Don't be sad. I need to know you're okay."

"I'm good, babe. I promise. Hey, I love you, but I have to go to work. I'll tell Uncle Dan you said hi!" she said, referring to my uncle who was the vice president of the grocery store where she worked.

"Please do! I love Uncle Dan. He's great!" I said.

Mindset

Six months under the sheets and I was getting comfortable as Steven. My paranoia level had lowered by a solid two notches down to an eight. I now regularly recognized myself as Steven without thought or process. My cover background was known and accepted by many, saving me from telling the lies over and over from week to week. I was comfortable with the processes and op-sec protocols even though they were time consuming and a pain in the ass. I made it past my initial wave of 007 excitement and battled through a round of what can only be classified as depression. I was comfortable in my acting role skin as Steven, but still knowing that I was Mac the undercover cop. Loneliness was my biggest enemy. I hadn't touched, hugged or even seen anyone that truly knew who I was for six months. Have you ever gone six months without having seen or touched any loved one or friends? Not even a handshake or a hug? It wore on me and was something I never even thought would be an issue when I agreed to enter the program.

Transition

It had been three months since I had seen Liz and that was cut short by the Chief's order. I hadn't seen any of my family or friends in over six months. I was hoping that Sam was going to handle my transition, but Mac luck, I got Jack. He was always a treat to see. My sarcasm rearing its ugly head there. Also, just for the record, because I can hear my boys here when they read this, *transition* just meant going from Steven's life back to Mac's; both I might add are heterosexual men. Back then, *transition* wasn't the

80

political buzz word used and glorified by this new left America. Now I sound like a true militia man.

No helicopters, secret car ports or popping smoke were involved in this transition. Jack picked me up and dropped me off at the local In-N-Out Burger near Mac's house. Driving there, I was nervous, which seemed a bit awkward to me. I hadn't seen everyone in over six months. I looked different, but was I different, I wondered? Exiting the freeway, all of the familiarities of home were comforting. The small things that I'd never thought would be comforting to me. A 7-Eleven where me and my buddies used to ride our bikes and buy Big Gulps. Funny, I thought. Jack pulled into the parking lot and grabbed the briefcase containing all of my stuff.

"I'm told all of your shit is in here. Take what you want," Jack said as he handed it to me. I opened it up and he was right, everything was in there to my surprise. Wow! My police badge, identification, and gun.

"I can take my badge and gun?" I asked.

Bothered by my question, Jack said, "Yeah, why wouldn't you? You're Mac the cop right now aren't you?"

The moment just caught me off guard and surprised me I guess. I took Mac's badge, gun and wallet and placed Steven's stuff back in the briefcase. "Meet me back here on Sunday at 1700 hours and don't be late," Jack said, as he folded back into his car and drove away. Just like that. *Mac was back, baby!*

Gary picked me up shortly after Jack left.

"Dude! You look homeless, man? What the fuck happened to you?" he said, laughing as he pulled up next to me in his Jeep CJ7. Looking back, I guess I did look like a homeless man in Gary's eyes, standing outside our favorite burger joint. Shoulder-length straggly hair, beard that I was constantly itching, holding an old duffle bag. Who knew that my hair was actually curly when I grew it out like a girl?

"What's up, man! It's great to see you," I said as I threw my bag over the roll bar and jumped in his jeep. He had the doors off just because it looked cool and that's what guys are always trying to do.

"Dude, I bet you could get a free burger looking like that. Hey, let's go get some cardboard and try it," Gary said, jokingly, but half seriously. "Tell me man. How's it going? What the fuck do they have you doing?"

"I don't want to talk about it right now, but all good, man. What's up with you? How's Mo, mom and dad?" I asked. Mo was a nickname I'd given Gary's last girlfriend. She was my favorite, but I don't think I ever told her that.

"Mo and I are done, man," he said, disappointedly.

"Whattttt! What did you do?" I asked, knowing that it had to be his fault because Mo adored him.

"I don't want to talk about it right now, but all good, man," he said mocking me brilliantly.

"Fair enough," I said, laughing.

"What's the plan? Do you have to stay inside or can we go out?" he asked.

"Hey, let's go up to the Rock and have some beers like old times?" I suggested.

"Really? I haven't been up there in years. Let's do it!" Gary was good like that. Full of life and always up for an adventure, living life in the moment.

"When are you seeing Liz?" he asked as we started driving.

"I'm not sure. I didn't tell her I was coming down yet. I wanted to surprise her and make it special," I said.

"I don't think that's a good idea, Mac, but what do I know. I suck at relationships." He shook his head as he laughed.

Gary and I stopped by our favorite 7-Eleven liquor store to grab a road kit before heading up to the Rock. I knew the Rock was a safe location; located in a secret location up in the mountains only locals knew about and police couldn't get to. The path, a dirt road only an experienced four-wheel driver could navigate. The destination, a huge boulder at the peak overlooking the Valley with a small stream navigating its way down the mountain nearby. Gary and I sat up at the rock for a few hours drinking a few beers, catching up on life, talking shit and telling lies just like we'd done since we were two years old. It energized me! I felt alive again and a *calmness* in my soul that I hadn't realized I was missing until that moment.

Gary and I were headed down the mountain when I heard several pages go off.

Beep, beep, beep… 939-2222. *Beep, beep, beep…* 939-2222222. It was Mick, the new guy. I ignored his page as Gary and I continued back to our house.

Beep, beep, beep… 939-3333. My pager went off again, but this time signaling code three, emergency. I opted not to tell Gary to pull over. We were only fifteen minutes away from our house and I didn't want to be bothered for once. As we pulled into the driveway: *beep, beep, beep…* 939-3333. Again! So much for that peace. It was gone and I was pissed.

"Mick. What's up?" I said, calling him from our home phone.

"Are you okay?" Mick said in a panic.

"Yeah. Why wouldn't I be? Dude, you guys are always fucking with me. Last time you came up and cut my trip short with Liz and now here you are again. Leave me alone!" I said, just venting, but it wasn't Mick's fault. He was new to the game.

"Hey, wait a minute. Listen to me. You were supposed to check in with me at 1700 hours and I haven't heard from you so I got worried," he explained.

"Mick, you didn't tell me to check in with you and neither did Jack. So how the fuck am I supposed to know that? Also, I'm on my own time for 72 hours. Just leave me alone," I said.

"Hey, Steven. I'm just doing what they told me, so I'm sorry for the miscommunication. I really apologize. I want you to have your own time. Just check in with me tomorrow at 1700 and that's it," Mick said with a sincere apology.

"Nope. I'm not doing that Mick," I said.

"What do you mean? You're not doing what? Mick asked, puzzled by my response.

"I'm not checking in with you tomorrow or any other day as Mac. I'll be code six on Sunday at 1700 hours, but that's it," I said, making an emotional decision trying to get back to that calmness.

"Steven. You have to check in with me tomorrow. It's the rules, man, and I don't make them!" Mick pleaded.

"Well, change the rules then because I'm not doing it," I said. There was a long pause and I could tell Mick was in a *pickle.* For me, I'd meant what I said, but more importantly, I wanted to see where Mick's loyalties lay.

84

"Steven. You don't get it. I am in charge of you. I am responsible for you and I'm telling you that you have to check in tomorrow," Mick said as I could sense his Irish blood begin to boil.

"Mick. This isn't going anywhere. We're going to have to *agree to disagree* on this one because I'm not checking in with you. It's my time," I said matter-of-factly.

"What the fuck, man. I'll come out and let's work this out, Steven. I'm asking you."

"Mick, I know you're new and you're just doing your job, but I'm not meeting you and I'm not checking in. That's it. We're going to have to *agree to disagree*. Do what you got to do. It's nothing personal, man. I get it. I just want my life back for seventy-two hours, then the Department can have me back. I'll be code six at the meet location on Sunday at 1700 hours. We can meet next week when I get back if you want. That's just how I feel. We'll talk next week when I get back," I said, hanging up the phone. I didn't think about it again. To this day, I have no idea what Mick did or didn't do; but I was never reprimanded, which I fully expected and probably deserved.

That night I slept so hard. My mind wasn't racing like most nights and I entered into what I can best describe as a coma-like sleep only to be awakened by a familiar smell and touch of a woman I so desired. My boy Gary let Liz in the house before he went off to work and there we were back in each others' arms with the smell of home-cooked Mexican breakfast lurking in the background. It made me question everything that I was doing and I never felt closer to Liz than in that moment. Finally, our emotional relationship was on equal ground and she saw me as vulnerable for the first time. I didn't want to let her go. I just wanted to lay there and hold her. So that's what we did until Sunday rolled around. Liz was scheduled to work that day but of course she called my Uncle Dan and he gave her the day off.

I spent my last several hours talking on the phone with my mom, dad, sister, Scooter and the rest of the gang. My family was going to make the trip down to see me but it seemed pointless since a holiday was around the corner. I said my goodbyes to everyone as my meet time was nearing. Gary dropped me off fifteen minutes early, but I felt energized and refreshed. Liz and I were in a great place, reaching a new level of commitment. Yes, I did question my choice about entering the program, but Liz helped me come to peace with it. We agreed, that if I could just get through the program we would have enough money to pay off our bills, buy a house and start our lives together. The program would also set me up with the Department for a great career and that meant I had no choice but to go back under the sheets.

Descanso Gardens

Located in the foothills just outside of the Los Angeles, 150 acres of prime real estate mostly forested, featuring artificial streams, ponds, a collection of fruit trees, flowers, and a ton of plants that I had never even heard of, let alone could pronounce. Mick's choice for our meet location.

Initially, I thought, what a strange place for a meet location. It was a bit of a drive from where I lived in the Valley. Wow was I wrong. If you've never been to Descanso Gardens, I would highly recommend it and I'm not really the environmental tree hugger type. This place was amazing. It was so beautiful and tranquil. I didn't really remember what Mick looked like, but it didn't matter. I saw him from a distance sitting on a bench, strategically located near the end of a dirt path. Cops can't help it and I don't really know what it is but our mannerisms give us away every time! Mick had a few cop *tell signs* that I saw: sunflower seed shells off to his right indicating that he had been there awhile, untucked Pendleton T-shirt, baseball cap, and a medal memorial band on his wrist. Many cops wear memorial bands honoring fellow officers who have paid the ultimate price.

Mick gave me the sign for the all clear to approach. I contemplated having a little fun with him and shaking off his sign, but common sense ruled and I reciprocated the all-safe sign. It would have been fun but I figured the way our last conversation ended the timing might be wrong.

"Steven. Nice to meet you man and thank you for making the drive," Mick said as he stood up. His handshake was firm, extending his trigger finger out straight. Steel blue eyes with an intense look, not quite the 1,000-mile stare often seen on suspects that are dusted, but close. Lips pursed. Voice inflection exuding confidence. Body language intense. My first impression of Mick hasn't wavered over the years; *this guy is wound really tight,* or to put it another way*, don't fuck with me or I'll kill you.*

"Hey Mick. Nice to meet you. This place is pretty cool," I said.

"Yeah, I researched it and thought it would be a great place to meet. I like it better, unless I'm hungry of course. A man has to eat." He paused. "I'm just going to be straight with you. I've only been in the division for three months and I'm just figuring things out myself, but I've heard a ton of great things about you and what you're doing. Some cool shit, man. Great job," Mick said even more intensely.

"Thanks man. I really appreciate it," I said, thinking, *wow, that was an actual compliment.*

"I don't know shit about terrorists, but I do know police work and how to put assholes in prison. I came from the South-end, codeword for *gunslinger* and I'm not afraid to work and that's what I am told this case needs," Mick said.

"No worries, Mick. Things are picking up for me so I think there will be plenty of work," I said.

"What do you need from me?" Mick asked.

"Nothing. I'm good," I said.

"So, you know Claire is on her way out and it's Al and I now. We'll be switching off on the on call every week. He'll have you one week and I'll have you the next. You know the drill."

"I do. Thanks Mick," I said.

"Sure you don't need anything from us?" Mick asked again, stumbling to make a good impression.

"Nope, I'm good," I said, feeling Mick out.

"Okay, cool. I reached out to your family and introduced myself. They're up to speed that they can go through me now instead of Claire. I gave them all of my contact numbers. I heard about your mom. I mean, I made sure your mom is good. She's good with me taking over," Mick said.

I broke character a bit, chuckling as Mick tried to explain my mother to me.

"Thanks, Mick. I appreciate it." Still chuckling inside but nodding my head in acknowledgment.

"I read your profile and I'm up to speed on your background. All great shit man," Mick said. "What do you want to know about me? Do you have any questions?"

"Are all the op sec protocols and rules the same? Do you have any new rules?" I asked.

"Listen, I'm not really a rules guy. Not in a criminal way or anything. I mean, the fewer the rules the better for me, because I'll forget them. So, no. Not that I know of. Business as usual."

"Okay, fair enough," I said.

"Hey? How's Al?" Mick asked.

"What do you mean?" I asked.

"How is he with you? Are you happy with him?" A bold question, I thought, for a guy who was so new to a coveted position.

"He's fine." Keeping my response short and my cards close to my chest.

Mick paused and I could tell that he wanted to call bullshit on my response, however, he didn't.

"Okay, fair enough," he said, mirroring my previous response to him.

I grinned.

"Hey? Tell me about these groups? Are they really good for something? I mean, what's their deal man?" Mick asked, switching gears.

"I don't know," I said.

"Yeah I know, but what do you think? I won't hold you to it, man," Mick said.

"I really have no idea," I responded, still holding my cards close to my chest but being honest.

"Well, let me ask you this. If you had to choose one who would it be?" Mick continued with his interrogation.

"I'm still pretty new, but they're starting to loosen up around me. Give me a few more months and that question will answer itself."

"Okay, if you don't have anything else let's get out of here," Mick said as he looked at his watch. "Listen, I can tell you're feeling me out and that's cool. But you need to know that I'm not fucking Al. You can trust me and that I have your back. If you call I'll fucking come. Anytime, anywhere! If you need anything, I'll bust my ass and make it happen. I swear to God." Mick made once last intense pitch to earn my trust before we shook hands again and parted ways.

The Department

A Look Behind the Curtain

Credit G

"The object of government in peace and in war is not the glory of rulers or of races, but the happiness of the common man."
William Beveridge

America was not ready for the bombing of the Murrah Federal Building. Law enforcement was caught off-guard, as were those who worked in the building, and those that lived in Oklahoma City and beyond. It was an inexplicable attack and a wholly unnecessary loss of human life, carried out by someone who supposedly loved this country. His was a twisted thought process, trying to save Americans from their own government by killing a mass of his fellow countrymen. The detonation of a vehicle-borne bomb attacking a government building on our own soil by an American exposed a nationwide intelligence vulnerability.

To be expected, the alarm sounded clearly throughout the intelligence community, police, and specifically the LAPD, where one of the nation's largest police forces staffed eighteen police stations spread throughout a sprawling landscape of 3.5 million people living in 464 urban square miles. The LAPD was more than just a dozen and a half police station houses. Scores more officers worked in other special coveted assignments, including its headquarters in downtown Los Angeles, Parker Center. It was here that its Anti-Terrorist Division (ATD) was housed in the western half of the building's seventh floor.

The Anti-Terrorist Division were once regarded as the *elite* of the *elite* within the intelligence community. In the early days ATD was known as the LAPD Intelligence Division, which became famous for collecting intelligence on politicians as well as organized crime figures and threats to the public order. The gathering of organized crime intel was meaningful and obtained in creative ways that was never talked about or seen amongst local law enforcement. Techniques such as a surveillance port inside an LAX terminal where countless out-of-town mob figures and associates were surreptitiously photographed shortly after deplaning. Others included

92

the establishment of a deep undercover program where undercover officers lived amongst their targets, politicos, and within the groups to gain first hand intelligence. One deep cover officer, an LAPD lieutenant, lived among communists in the USSR for a twelve-year period during the Parker era. Not much is known of the value realized by LAPD by this prolonged residency, but it certainly was LAPD's effort to participate in the Cold War, and undoubtedly played into prohibiting Nikita Khrushchev from visiting Disneyland in 1959. The use of deep cover undercover officers only spoken of as '*The Program*' was so secret not even the mayor knew of its existence back then.

The political intel gathered by the undercover officers was sometimes deployed by LAPD's long serving Chief William Parker as *capital* in all kinds of transactions. For as much as Parker and the FBI's J. Edgar Hoover didn't get along, Parker successfully utilized Hoover's tactics on local politicos. Much later, Parker's Intelligence Division was broken up into the Organized Crime Intelligence Division (OCID) and the Public Disorder Intelligence Division (PDID), the predecessor of the Anti-Terrorist Division.

The widespread power to collect information on politicians, particularly those linked to, or suspected of association with, the Communist party, was eventually exposed and leaked to the media. The result: the Chief's elite PDID was *slapped* by the Police Commission, setting new strict guidelines on what the intelligence division could gather information on. The new regulations required PDID to receive permission from the Police Commission prior to investigating any groups like militias. Specifically, PDID had to provide proof that a group was capable of and had the desire to threaten, attempt, plan, or perform a significant disruption of the public order. If PDID was successful in their efforts to provide proof, then and only then would the Commission approve or *qualify* the group and the LAPD would add them to their own terrorist watch list. But until such time that the secret blessing of the Police Commission was bestowed, PDID *could not* collect intelligence on any group. The catch-22 felt by investigators was that without intelligence, the group likely could not be *qualified.* How is the group qualified if detectives can't gather intelligence, and since the group isn't *qualified,* intelligence can't be gathered. A misstep, where civilian oversight and politicos make law enforcement policy, seemingly handcuffing PDID. The Public Disorder Intelligence Division was scarred, disarmed, and rendered useless by the hammer of the Commission, however the program survived. A few years later, PDID's name was changed to the Anti-Terrorist Division hoping for a revival.

For as vaunted and daunting as its name once was, the newly named Anti-Terrorist Division had become a low-functioning assemblage of detectives who hid their inabilities and inactivity behind restrictions issued by the civilian oversight body and the Los Angeles Police Commission. On April 19, 1995, the staffing level of ATD was less than 50% of its authorized strength. Of that 50%, few held themselves accountable to LAPD's mantra of 8 for 8. Simply put, the expectation was 8 hours of meaningful work for 8 hours pay. Largely this was lost on the *elite,* now folklore, of detectives who were assigned to the anti-terrorism capability of the nation's third largest police department. Many used the time to swim, run, lift weights, watch their kids' t-ball games, sip Starbucks and sell ATD logo-wear. Everybody had a gig that LAPD was passively funding. To further confound ATD, those that remained in its ranks from the PDID days fiercely defended their lack of work ethic and inexplicable lack of expertise. "We get paid for what we know, not what we do." Management didn't know what they *didn't* know, including the fact that there was very little knowledge of terrorists and terrorism held by ATD anymore.

Remaining current on terrorist threats, both foreign and domestic, was the charge of ATD. However, at the time of the bombing, very little was known about militias which translated to a discernible inability to accurately calculate the risk posed to Los Angeles and its environs. Timothy McVeigh shocked everyone awake. LA's mayor certainly interrupted the napping ATD folk, demanding answers. The Anti-Terrorist Division had none and was forced to rely on the private sector, more specifically a pair of Non-Government Organizations (NGOs) that monitored hate groups. Embarrassed and exposed, it was a sad truth that an *elite* police entity with top secret clearances had been inadequately positioned to rely on their own powers and abilities compared to the likes of two non-profits. Both NGOs went to press early with analyses of the militia movement, including information on potential bad actors specific to regions of the country. ATD was nowhere to be found. Lost by ROAD (Retired On Active Duty) personnel.

Pissed, the mayor ordered ATD up to full staff. The LAPD scrambled to interview, select and complete background investigations on candidates. Current ATD personnel began chasing tips and responding to tasking from federal agencies since they didn't have any intelligence of their own. Some detectives were nothing more than clue clowns, which was oddly an upgrade from the at-large clownery they were generally known for. The LAPD's truly informed knew that the supposed *elite* terrorism investigators were more a troop of motley fools than a platoon of protectors.

The Chief also heard the mayor and polled ATD about the militia movement. Anti-Terrorist Division detective supervisors advanced a line of pure bullshit to cover up the lack of intelligence on militias, but what they couldn't do was cover up the fact that there were no deep cover infiltrators in any militia group. Some realized the gigging had to stop or at least subside, including the Chief.

A newly assigned captain was put in charge of ATD to fulfill the mayor's and the Chief's demands. The new captain was clear; he wanted to eliminate a reliance on other intelligence sources, chiefly federal agencies that were notorious for their unwillingness to share information with each other, the public and law enforcement partners. And second, he wanted workers to fill the ample vacancies. This included the deep cover operative who would be re-directed from the KKK to the militia movement, *Drew*.

The invasion of a new generation of ATD investigators was quick, refreshing or disturbing depending on which side of the fence you were on. With their arrival was a commitment to delve into the militia movement, increase understanding, apply known and proven investigative methods and information for the purposes of more adequately protecting LA's populace. The 8 for 8 mantra was in full force and the *gigging* was ridiculed by the new generation. It was a revolution.

The nascence of the militia movement served as a temporary hiding ground for the old guard. Intel morsels were passed along to the LAPD higher-ups. A piecemeal patchwork peddled by the unmotivated, uncreative and uncommitted seemed to mollify the civilian overseers. As long as every other Wednesday promised a paycheck to ATD's ergophobes, trivia and tidbits, accurate or not, about militias would be the consistent diet of intelligence fed to the Police Commission. Unbeknown to the Commission, much of the intelligence they were receiving was open source. LAPD was paying for recitation of opinion pieces, news stories and information gathered from watchdogs. ATD personnel passed it off as intelligence as a means of justifying their existence.

And then came Drew...

He posed his own threat but didn't know it. He was sold the *old guard's elite mantra* and was all in. His presence stood the chance of exposing the unproductive and unknowing, particularly if Drew successfully penetrated a militia or militias. More fright was generated by the soon-to-be realized workstream an active and talented deep cover officer would create. None of the old guard was up to it and threw up road blocks when possible. Drew was an unyielding rate buster. The movement demanded it; ATD scorned it.

Drew's old guard handlers were in a pickle. Stunned by his multiple immediate successes penetrating militia groups, they applauded it to his face but scoffed at it on the golf course, knowing what was coming. As the nation began to report on the evolution of truly armed militia groups there came the more aggressive pursuit of information by newly assigned ATD personnel. Drew began to identify Southern California paramilitary groups, their membership, and their methods of operating in Los Angeles. Organizational commonality and similarity to known terrorist movements was identified. While each militia had its own oddities and eccentricities, the same was true of its membership. The common bond was present, but so were other likes and dislikes. Some were defined by personality, others by locale and still more by financial status. All had some level of disenfranchisement, many had an avowed hatred for the government, which emerged from different drivers. Income tax, border security, perceived communist threats, were paired with conspiracy theories related to alleged government surveillance of its own people. Black helicopters, implanted microchips, surveillance via laptops, televisions and cell phones were beliefs promulgated and pursued. There were broad conspiracies afoot to suppress and disarm the American people and the conspirators were both foreign and domestic. The evidence was undeniable and could no longer be hidden. There was a considerable workload to be undertaken on the militia cases as the workload would self-multiply across the knowledge axis. The more Drew uncovered, the more work was generated. That work took them to places and people heretofore unknown. Along the way a simple truth was revealed.

LA had a militia problem…

Ramp Up

"Courage is almost a contradiction in terms.
It means a strong desire to live taking
the form of a readiness to die."
G.K. Chesterton

The militia movement continued to catch fire across the country and I seemed to be placed right smack in the middle of it. Militia meetings or events several days a week, along with five days of actual work to pay the bills, operational or firearms training at night with an occasional weekend, then add a debrief for everything that I'd attended. The pace was fast and unbearable at times. Just a few months earlier, I would get excited about identifying a new member or especially a new militia cell. Now it seemed routine and hard to keep track of in my mind. My militia reach was extending throughout the Nation. On the bright side, my confidence as an undercover officer was high. My observation skills, attention to detail, and my ability to read the room were top notch. Surprisingly, my memory capacity had doubled from six months prior. The deeper I sank into the militia movement, the better I became and the more lost I was as Mac. Sleeping became one of my largest challenges. My mind wouldn't stop. Always looking over my shoulder, peace eluded me.

Rainier Park Patriot Group

The Rainier Park Patriot Group became my core militia even though our group would attend both the KLC and Denali Park militia group meetings and training. We were meeting one to three times a week including an occasional weekend training day, wherever we could find one. The group was growing slowly every week, but struggled expanding its core membership group. I would describe the core membership as eclectic religious historians who had never played Cowboys and Indians as a child, charged a hill, nor knew anything about detonating a truck bomb, but were over the top fanatical batshit crazy.

There were Jeff and Kelly, an engaged couple; think Lewis from *Revenge of the Nerds* meets MaryAnn from *Gilligan's Island* with a Plumeria flower behind her left ear. An odd couple by appearance, but who I am to judge love? Jeff, oversized feet that swayed abnormally outward, a lumbering walk for such a thin build. Black thick hair with a slightly off centered middle part, feathered, but not like Shawn Cassidy. More like the greasers. Spoke with uncanny confidence, derived from his intellect and not his athletic prowess. He struck me as an extra in a commercial, forgettable; not the main character.

Kelly was strikingly more attractive than her fiancé even if the bar was low. Never seemed to be on his level of intellect. A mail order bride was my first impression. Confused by her bloodline, but I later tagged her as Polynesian. Skin, golden brown, blemish free, dressed modestly and seemed to walk in Jeff's shadow. Well-groomed down to her toes, make-up free. Anticipation overtook me waiting for her arrival to each meeting to see if her signature Plumeria flower behind her left ear would be present.

Profiling? This isn't the face of the narrative that I see on the news or have been fed through various intelligence reports. Where are the gun-toting, white supremacist militia members that hate America and all beings that are not white? How would Americans feel if they saw the face of Kelly as the real militia?

Tom called me up shortly after a meeting where we were discussing *prepping*. A term that meant to prepare for that moment when the government was going to launch the final phase of the *New World Order's* plan and attempt to take Americans' guns.

"Hey Steven, it's Tom. I just saw a Big 5's ad and they have SKS rifles on sale next weekend for $79. And the ammo is on sale too," he said excitedly.

"Really? Where is it on sale at?" I asked.

"Big 5. I'm going to go grab two I think. I believe they're considered relics or historical rifles so there isn't any waiting period. Don't quote me on that, but I believe that's true," Tom said.

"What's an SKS rifle? Will it work for us?" I asked.

"It was Russia's primary weapon back in the day. It shoots the same rifle round as the AK47. It has a bayonet fixed to the front and has a multiple round clip. Hell, yeah they will work. What I like about them is that they're rugged. You don't have to baby them and they'll shoot," Tom went on.

"Okay, cool. I want to check them out. When are you going?" I asked.

"The sale starts next Saturday, so I'm going to be there when they open. I know they'll sell out. Are you working or do you want to go together?" Tom asked me.

"That's my department's big sale that weekend and if I'm not there my boss will kill me, but I might be able to go in a little late. I'll let you know at our next meeting," I said and Tom agreed.

Tom called me early the next day and asked me if I could host the meeting at my apartment. I said yes. I wasn't sure if that was right or wrong. Within Department policy or not? I decided right then and there that I was no longer going to worry about policy and procedures and just *be*. Mick had the on-call that week so I called to let him know about the change.

"What's up? You okay?" Mick's standard response after an unscheduled page from me.

"Yup. All good. Hey, Tom called me and wanted me to host tonight's meeting at my place," I said.

"Oh shit. Why? What's that about?" Mick asked in rapid succession.

"No idea. He just called me and asked," I said.

"Oh. You didn't ask why?" Mick asked.

"No. Why would I?" I asked.

"Hell. I don't know. Just thinking out loud here. Can you, I mean we, do that?" Mick asked.

"No idea. But we're doing it tonight," I said, as we both started to laugh.

"Oh great. Fuck it. Let's do it. I'll handle it on my end. What do you need from me?"

"Hey, just a heads up. The main topic of our meeting tonight is going to be for the group to start to *arm* ourselves. Big 5 is having a sale on SKS rifles next weekend and Tom wants our group to buy some. I'm not sure what the Department's posture is going to be. All the politics, liabilities, red tape, etc. But it needs to happen on my end. I have to buy a rifle and some ammo," I said.

"The rifle is an SKS?" Mick asked.

"Yeah, that's what he said, but I'm not really a gun guy so I have no idea what that is," I said.

"I've shot that rifle. It's old, but it's bad ass. I think it fires the same round as the AK," Mick continued to think out loud.

"Yup. That's it. Tom said the same stuff," I said, recognizing Mick's superior knowledge of weapons.

"Wait. Did you say the meeting tonight is about the group arming themselves? Did Tom say that?" Mick asked.

"No. He didn't say that directly, but I know him pretty well and that's my guess," I said.

"Okay, so he didn't say that? Because I don't want to report that if he didn't say it," Mick clarified.

"No, Mick, he didn't say it." I laughed.

"Hey. If they're coming to your place it needs to be *dry cleaned*. You know they're going to check your shit out," Mick said like a worried father.

"I'm good. It's clean," I reassured him.

"Cool. I'll let you know. The 6th floor is going to shit themselves that there's a meeting tonight about a militia group arming themselves in the city. And that one of their *birds* is hosting the meeting. I love it!" Mick said.

Ironically, there were five in attendance at the Big 5 meeting: Tom, Jeff, Kelly, Mike and myself. The crazy things I thought of prior to hosting my first of many militia meetings: Do I need to go get snacks? What about drinks or cocktails?

Suffering from slight OCD, and blaming my mother for this one who always kept a tidy house. Was my apartment too clean? I thought. One after another, my fellow militia comrades showed up, pads and pens in their hands. Except for Tom, who always wore a fanny pack around his waist. He came along with a special gift. I'm going to call it a hosting party gift: a twenty-pound bag of white rice. Before the meeting started:

"Hey, Steven. Do you mind unplugging your telephone and disconnecting your television?" Tom asked me.

"No. I don't mind." Wandering what craziness that was about, but I didn't ask.

"Great. Thank you. You know the government can listen in through those lines?" Tom said.

Listen through a cable line, I thought to myself?

"I didn't know that. Thanks for letting me know," I said.

The meeting started off like every other meeting with an opening prayer. However, tonight's prayer was poignant.

"Welcome everyone and thank you once again for coming. Steven, thank you for hosting tonight," Tom led off. "Let's bring the meeting to order and start off with a prayer because we will need God's strength and wisdom to fight this enemy. In Numbers 21:3, God commands us to arm ourselves to execute the Lord's vengeance. Which in this case God is speaking about the *New World Order*. The verse reads: *So, Moses spoke to the people, saying, 'Arm men from among you for the war, that they may go against The New World Order to execute the Lord's vengeance on The New World Order.'*" Tom closed his bible before he continued.   "And that's exactly what we need to do, but before we get into it, let's open with the Pledge of Allegiance." Tom looked towards me as I realized… I didn't have an American Flag in my apartment! Oops. We ended up pledging our allegiance to a small American patch on Tom's jacket we hung from a stand-alone chair.

The agenda seemed extremely long tonight as I began to calculate in my head how long I would have these people in my apartment. In the single small living room, Jeff and Kelly were sitting on my couch. Tom and Mike sat on two fold-up chairs and I sat on the floor near the front door. The first agenda item was that Tom had identified three additional recruits he wanted to invite to a meeting, but he was seeking our permission first. He handed the group a manilla folder containing each recruit's name along with their basic personal information. Nothing extraordinary or that I would consider a full background check. The group perused the future recruits' information and nodded their heads.

The next agenda item was the upcoming rifle and training exercise hosted by the Denali Park and KLC militias.

"I would like to propose that we buy these SKS rifles and attend the training exercise," Tom said, looking around at the room to view everyone's response.

No one said anything.

"I'm good with it," I said, breaking the silence, knowing that it would make my job easier being able to watch all the groups at once. Shockingly, everyone followed my lead without objection.

"Let's vote on it to make it official. Say aye or nay," Tom said out loud, looking at me first before he continued clockwise around the room.

"Aye."

"Aye."

"Aye."

"Aye."

"And I'm an Aye also. Let's take a ten-minute break," Tom said, asking to use my bathroom.

Boom! There it was. The bathroom request. I would have been disappointed if he or the others hadn't asked to use my bathroom. After all, I didn't clean the toilet for them but were they or he in this case, really going to the bathroom to urinate? Or was it just a ploy to snoop around in my cabinets, like I would do? However, I'd rigged my cabinets so I would know if they'd been opened. *You did what?* I'm sure you are asking. Or maybe, *How did you rig your cabinet doors?* It depends on the door, but in this case I placed a toothpick in the seam of the bottom of the door and a small piece of paper out of view in the other. If the door was opened, the toothpick and/or small piece of paper would fall to the ground and it is extremely hard to see or even know its true purpose.

During the break, I warmed up some old pizza that I had in the fridge along with my grandmother's recipe sweet tea I'd made earlier in the day. Only Tom took me up on the pizza, but my grandma's sweet tea was a hit.

"Okay everyone, let's continue with the agenda," Tom said, not knowing he had pizza sauce on the side of his face.

"Next on the agenda is *preparation*," Jeff said.

"Yes. As we opened up in prayer with. I believe it is not only *God's will*, but *his command* that it's time we arm ourselves to fight this new enemy. We need to not only arm ourselves, but we need to train and prepare. Now I know many of us are not well armed except for Ralph who could probably arm us all," Tom said with a chuckle followed by the rest of the group's acknowledgement. "But, Big 5 is having a great sale next weekend on a rifle that will work for us. It's called a SKS and it fires the same round as the AK47. The price is right. Just under $100. It's a great starter weapon for us to arm ourselves. I would recommend buying two if you can afford it. One that you will use and a second that we can cache at a safe location. The ammo is also going to be on sale too," Tom continued.

"I'm going to buy two, Tom. One each for Kelly and me. But how much ammo are you going to buy?" Jeff asked.

"I'm going to buy 1,000 rounds if I can and I would recommend the same for everyone," Tom said.

"Steven, what about you?" Jeff asked me.

"Yeah, I talked to Tom earlier. I plan on buying one but I'm scheduled to open that morning. Still trying to figure it out," I responded.

"Does anyone have any objections to arming ourselves?" Tom asked.

"Hell no! We're a fucking militia. I mean we're a patriot group. It's our duty to arm ourselves," Ralph exclaimed.

"Hey. Let's try and get there early, but I don't want anyone to act like we know each other. I'm sure that the ATF will be there taking names and I don't want them to connect us. Does everyone agree?" Tom asked and the group agreed.

"We have a few more things on my agenda. Let me see what's next," Tom said as he looked down at a printed agenda. The title of the document read, "The Rainier Park Patriot Group." "We all need to be able to get ahold of each other so I propose we all get pagers. I looked into pricing and it costs $12 a month. I know that may be a lot of money for you all but I believe it's necessary," Tom continued, but the group agreed and didn't push back on his suggestion. "Let's talk about codes and meet locations," he said. Over the next hour we decided on the following:

Call Signs		Meet Locations	
Tom	55	01	Lyons Exit off of the 5 frwy
Jeff	66	02	Steven's Apartment

Kelly	77	03	Jeff's House	
Mike	88	04	KLC Compound	Steven 99

Alerts

711	Test	09	Meet
11	Red Alert	10	Call – Important
22	Yellow Alert	07	Cancel
33	Green Alert	123	Call to Arms

Tom was pleased with our progress and told us that we were to commit the codes to memory, announcing there would be a test at our next meeting. Everyone seemed pleased and felt accomplished. Tom was on a roll tonight, checking off items on his agenda.

"Next, I have positions or duties. We need to vote and break up duties both administratively and operationally. Since we're a paramilitary unit let's vote on rank structures here. Does anyone object to me being the commander?" Tom said, and no one objected.

Over the next hour we went over several different roles realizing that those roles would change as we grew in number and strength. But for now, we decided the following:

Operational		**Administrative**	
Commander	Tom	Recruitment	Tom/Jeff
Assist Commander	None	Scribe	Kelly
Radio Officer	Jeff	Communications	Steven
Logistics	Kelly	Security	Jeff
Sniper	Steven		

We ended the meeting going through Tom's remaining items, which were small. It was a big meeting for the group and we all knew it. Our first major steps towards organization and arming ourselves. I was right about one of the purposes of the meeting but I missed the mark overall. The group was organizing and arming quickly and I knew that once I debriefed Mick the 6th floor boys were going to get their panties ruffled. It was a long mentally draining meeting and I was hungry since Tom had eaten the rest of my pizza. *Beef Bowl here I come*, I thought.

I drove down a few of my secret routes that would expose a tail just in case before heading over to the Beef Bowl for a late snack. Once my food was ordered I stepped outside to the payphone to check in with Mick.

Ring, ring, ring…

"Hey Mick!" I said, wide awake.

"Damn, dude. That was a long one. I was falling asleep. Jules kept yelling at me to wake up," Mick said.

"Wait? Are you allowed to tell your wife about me?" I asked.

"No. But she knows if Steven calls. It's important. Go get me. And don't ask any questions. She also knows when it's my week on call and not to schedule anything," Mick said.

"Got it," I said.

"Well? How did it go?" Mick asked.

"It was so long, man. I was dying. Jeff and Kelly sat on my couch and I can't get their smell off it. Terrible, man. You guys don't pay me enough for this shit," I said.

Laughing, Mick asked again, "What happened?"

110

"We voted to buy the rifles this weekend and arm ourselves. Tom also said he has three new dudes that he wants to bring to the next meeting," I said before Mick cut me off.

"No shit! Wow, that's huge. Hey, can you debrief tonight?"

"Really? What time is it?" I asked.

"I don't know. Jules! What time is it, babe?" Mick yelled and I heard 10:30 come firing back through the phone.

"It's 10:30 and you want to debrief?" I asked Mick.

"I do! Can you do it?" Mick asked.

"If you're in. I'm in," I said.

"I can meet you in thirty minutes. Where do you want to meet?" Mick asked.

"Meet me at the Denny's by my apartment at 11," I said.

Mick showed up at the Denny's five minutes early. He must have driven one hundred miles an hour to get from the South Bay to the Valley in twenty-five minutes. The benefit and curse of having a take-home police car, I guess. We went through our op sec protocols before we sat down. I didn't eat or even order any food to go this time. My stomach cursing me with every churn. The beef bowl with white rice, drowned in teriyaki sauce, always tasted better than it was received.

Mick's style of debriefing was very different from Al's. Mick wrote everything down in a book. And I mean everything, word for word. Full sentences. Quotes. If I'd heard it, he wrote it down. I saw the clock tick past 1 AM. Mick shaking his right hand now after every sentence was completed. Talking to himself. Repeating the information I'd told him over and over as he wrote it on paper. Me chiming in and correcting him on occasion. Mick then reading back what he'd written to ensure its accuracy.

"Hey. That's some great info. Anything else you can think of?" Mick asked.

"No. I think that's it, man," I answered, both of us exhausted.

"Here. Just read over everything and make sure it's right then we'll initial and date it at the bottom," Mick said.

"Really?" I asked. "I've never done that before."

"I know, but we are from now on, okay?" Mick said. "I got that from our analyst, G. He knows this shit, man, and has been helping me."

"G? Like the letter?" I asked with a chuckle.

"Yup. It's a nickname obviously. But he's been a great help bringing me up to speed," Mick said.

"Analysis? What does he do?" I asked.

"So G takes all of the intelligence from all the sources. It could be from the FBI, ATF, news articles, speakers. Wherever he can get it. He tracks it. Builds profiles, compiles reports, etc. It's cool shit," Mick said.

"Oh wow. I didn't know that," I said.

"Yeah, G is the one that told me we need to start documenting all of your meetings. Write everything down and have you initial it once it's accurate."

"Make sense to me now," I said.

"What's your schedule tomorrow?" Mick asked.

"I have to go in at 7. Then I have the Granada Forum tomorrow night," I said.

"Okay. I'll let you know how we're going to handle the gun purchase tomorrow. If you can, maybe we can meet after work before you go to the Forum? I'll buy you lunch."

"Sounds good. We'll talk tomorrow. Drive safe, man," I said as we parted ways.

Mick and I began to gel and earn each other's trust. Cops often speak of trust. But I never really understood it until this assignment. It's such a vague word. Trust – that doesn't fully engulf the magnitude of what cops mean when they speak of it. Civilians wouldn't understand it at that level, but speak of it as if they do. Trust in a cop's world means: *Will you show up if I need you? Under any circumstances? Unconditionally? At any cost?*

For the first time, I didn't feel like I had to worry about both sides of the equation: *the Department* and *the Militia*. Instinctually, I felt my interest and concerns were Mick's. He believed what I was telling him about the explosion of the militia movement and conveyed my messages to the Command staff, unfiltered to a fault at times, I would later learn. He was excited about the case and wasn't afraid to work. He was a problem solver and not an obstacle setter. We were partners.

Denali Park Militia

The Denali Park militia had been together for a while so they were more advanced than the Rainier Park militia cell. They had a core militia group that was larger, had experienced members with firearms training, preparation, and organizationally they were further along. However, they seemed more focused on the intelligence, conspiracy theory side compared to truck bomb go shoot them up type. Think men's bible study group, but replace the Bible with the *Turner Diaries* and a side arm. Ideally, the KLC militia wanted our two groups to become militia cells under their group, becoming LA #1 (Rainier Park militia) and LA#2 (Denali Park militia). Denali Park militia's direction was to train our group. Our first joint training exercise was upcoming and the Denali Park militia was holding a meeting at Jason's place to go over the training exercise along with knife training taught by David Hoss, the crazy black guy in what the public believes is a white man's racist militia. *How fitting*, I thought to myself. The training orders sent to our group instructed us to bring a folding bladed knife and an extra t-shirt.

The training had already started by the time I arrived. I don't recall the reason why I was tardy to such an important event, but LA traffic is always a safe fallback. The core group, who I referred to as the founding fathers of the Denali Park militia, were there: Jason (J), Kevin, Johnny, Ralph, along with our Rainier Park militia cell. And the main character for the night, David. Also, in attendance were six other gents that I had never seen before. It was a bit overwhelming walking in late. A mistake duly noted in my mind.

David was standing on the living room couch using it as a stage. Desert military boots, camo pants, brown long sleeve undershirt, not to be outdone by the matching camo jacket. If he were to lie down on that shit brown couch he might disappear, I thought. Holding a knife with his left hand, pick-handle-style with the blade tucked tightly against his forearm concealing it. His stance was bladed and his body movements were fluid. I could tell that he had some level of training, formal or informal, based on his awareness of the blade without having to look. This dude is oozing crazy, I thought. It's always the left handers that… but wait, this guy crushes my hand every time with his right…?

114

"Steven, you're late. Everyone's paired up so you're with me I guess," David yelled, not from on top of the mountain, but on top of the couch in this case.

"Okay. Sure," I said, but thinking to myself, *that's Mac luck right there*. I always get stuck with the crazy or the fat smelly dude sitting next to me on the plane.

"Okay, imagine someone has grabbed you from behind and has a knife to your throat. Let me show you how to get out of it. Steven, do you mind?" David asked, motioning me to be his dummy. Which proved to be true.

"Sure. What do you want me to do?" I asked, looking at David who was still standing on the couch.

He jumped down from the couch as he switched the knife to his right and walked behind me to demonstrate the training technique. He reached around my neck with his left arm and secured his hold by grabbing a handful of my shirt on my right shoulder. I felt his right forearm on the side of my neck where the knife was, but I didn't feel the blade against my skin. The pressure on my carotid arteries along both sides of my neck began to build from firm pressure, but he wasn't squeezing. When he secured his left-hand grip with my t-shirt I could feel him wrap my shirt's material around his fingers to lock his grip, just as I would. His technique was good, especially since I was taller than him. It's always harder to choke out a taller guy without mounting his back and wrapping your legs. I felt the sweat of his head on the left side of my face as he tucked his head up against mine. *This guy's pretty good*, I thought to myself, *but he stinks or at least smells funny*. The squirrel family in my head woke up and began to run around as I realized the craziest motherfucker in the room had me

115

locked in a choke with a knife to the side of my neck. And I'd let him. *Good job, Mac*, I told one of the squirrels running around in my brain.

"If anyone gets you in this hold with a knife you're dead," David said. It was as if he'd read my thoughts, but instinctually I didn't feel threatened. I don't know why.

"But we're not teaching this tonight. Another time," David said.

David went on to teach basic knife defense techniques for about thirty minutes. As I watched the other men in the group train, it was easy to for me to start to build a profile on each of the members and to prioritize my targets.

Jason had previous weapons training not only with a knife but with a weapon would be my guess. His movement was fluid and I saw a side arm on him which he motioned to once with his trigger finger outstretched alongside of the gun frame. It made sense to me. He was most likely a former Army Ranger.

Kevin, a tubular man with long straggly hair, seemed gentle as a giant but couldn't move that well. He could give two shits about this training and seemed very disinterested, taking several trips to the room to the north, kitchen.

Johnny… Johnny… Johnny – dad bod, with high energy, loud mouth, and a know it all. Think New Yorker here without the accent. He picked up the training quickly and seemed very eager to learn the offensive techniques even though David wasn't teaching those tonight. Intuitively, I moved him up in my target rankings.

Ralph, my instinct was he was their gear guy. Everyone knows one of these guys and Ralph I thought was it for this group. This guy had gadgets dangling off of every pock and limb of his body. A compass, water filtration system, pepper spray, 550 cord bracelet, and at least three knives that I saw. I was certain he had a few other items concealed.

"Someone tell me again, why would we bring a knife to a gun fight?" Ralph asked, and the other members shouted in agreement.

"If the balloon goes up it's not going to be a knife fight, boys," Johnny chimed in.

"Don't worry, Ralph, we're doing weapons training soon. You can shoot something then," Jay said.

As the training continued, David showed the group how to wrap our t-shirts around our defensive arm/hand to provide a layer of protection. I couldn't help but wonder as David was teaching how many people had actually been in a real knife fight because I had never even heard of one.

He went on to teach the group how to hold and use your shirt/jacket as a shield and/or blocking tool. It was actually pretty cool training, I thought as the night ended, and I felt really good. My nerves were calm. I had been able to build out the founding fathers' profiles in my brain and restructure my target list. Any night, even in training, where you walk away after having a knife to your throat, I would call a success.

Field Training Exercise

A few days later, the group received a page from Tom: 09-01, signaling he wanted the group to meet at the Lyons exit off of the 5 freeway. I was not happy about the page because it seemed we were traveling in the wrong direction. It was a Friday, and the traffic in and around Los Angeles is always challenging. This training exercise was being held in the Mojave Desert, near mile marker 88 of the old Mojave trail. I arrived early to our meet location, so I grabbed a quick bite to eat at the nearby In-N-Out Burger. Soon, the rest of our group arrived along with the Denali Park militia. It seemed our group was slightly on edge, but I couldn't pinpoint the cause. We caravanned together, traveling in trail, slowly and methodically. There were thirteen in our caravan, but I knew we were expecting to meet more militia members from the KLC group at the training site in the morning.

Jason, driving the lead vehicle, turned off onto a dirt road several hours later. The sun had already left the skies for the night, but it was clear, giving the stars a clear path to light up our final resting point. We set up camp in the darkness. My camp consisted of a simple sleeping bag and a tent. Others were much more extravagant: tents, canopies, stoves, lights, and portable heaters. It was interesting to see which militia member brought what. Interestingly enough, I did not see any firearms present. Everyone claimed their own dirt spots, giving each other plenty of privacy. Tom wanted our group to stay together so me, Jeff, Kelly, Tom, and Mike set up fairly close to each other. After everyone was settled, I went out to gather some firewood. I thought it might get a bit cold and I didn't have a portable heater.

I woke up to rainfall hitting my tent and water trickling inside my tent. The wind was bone-chilling, whipping, but I couldn't find the hole in my tent. Poking my head out like a turtle, I didn't see anything stirring except for the dirt, nor did I see too many other options for me. Returning my head to the warmth and dryness I hoped this was a quick desert cry from the gods above. The rain continued in duration and increased in sheer volume. Eventually mother nature won the battle like she often does and my tent was flooded and my sleeping bag was a sponge.

"Steven. Steven. Come in our tent," I heard Kelly say, motioning with her hand. I really didn't want to. It just seemed odd to me. Their tent was small and I didn't want to be inside their personal crazy space, even as an undercover officer.

"It's okay. I'm good. I'm going to just get up," I said. Puzzled by my response, Kelly closed the door of their tent and went back to bed. Me on the other hand, I was up, but not too wet considering. Thankfully the rain slowed and eventually stopped with the sunrise. Morning arrived quicker than I had expected and Jason provided everyone a briefing of the weekend's training.

TRAINING AGENDA

Operational Training

- o   Survival Training
- o   Equipment – H-Rig, V-Rig, Load outs
- o   Topography Map Reading
- o   Compass – True North vs Compass North
- o   Desert Patrol Tactics – Wedge formations, danger zones
- o   Security Details

Administrative

- o   MML Machine
- o   Security Update – trash searches, snitches
- o   Russian Forces Training in the United States
- o   Black Helicopters

Before the training started, several members of the KLC militia showed up: Paul leading the charge, with Commander Joel and his son Zach in trail. Dean, the KLC head of security, along with Mike, a guy I had never even heard of let alone seen. Once everyone was settled with cups of fresh brewed coffee the training started. Jason from the Denali Park militia and former Army Ranger was the lead instructor. He brought out his packs, sometimes referred to as his 'load outs', before passing out an equipment list handout to the group. Jason went over his basic survival pack, which took about an hour. Some of the items he covered were:

- Battle dress uniforms: Desert, Wooded, and Black
- Boots
- Cold weather gear
- Knives
- Fire starters
- Signaling device
- Fishing line
- 550 Cord
- Flint/fire starter
- Glass (Binoculars)
- Multi Tool
- Camel pack
- Water filter
- Gloves
- Chem lights
- Compass
- MRE (Meals Ready to Eat)

The next training topic was land navigation using a compass and a topography map. I had never even seen a topography map before and I definitely didn't know there was so much to using a compass. I thought you just pointed in a certain direction and then you walked. Not so much the case… Do you know how to shoot an azimuth? Did you know that there is a difference between *true north* and *magnetic north* and why that's important? Have you ever thought about if you're walking and trying to follow a map, how do you calculate how far you've walked? No cell phones here. I believe your answer is most likely like mine: absolutely not!

Jason taught the group how to read a compass, shoot an azimuth and how to count your steps using a system called 'ranger beads'. The training was fascinating to me. I loved it.

Jason called out to the group, "Okay, everyone. See this stake with an orange ribbon on it and you'll see another one along this trail that's 0.05 miles away," he said, pointing down the trail about 100 yards. "I want everyone to walk at a normal pace and count your steps between both stakes. Do that twice. Then average your step count," he said as the group headed off to count their steps.

My average step count for 0.05 miles was 100 steps. The picture below represents an example of ranger beads. Here is how they are used. With map in hand, you start walking counting your steps along your journey. As soon as I count 100 steps, I slide one of the nine lower beads down to the bottom of the knot. I keep counting my steps until I reach another 100 steps, then slide a second lower bead down to the knot. I repeat the process until all nine beads have reached the bottom. After the tenth time, I know that I have traveled 1,000 steps or a half of a mile. I now know that I have traveled a half of a mile, so I slide one of the top beads down to the bottom and reset my lower beads to the top, starting the process over. Every time I get to 1,000 steps, I slide another top bead down and start over again until all of my top beads are gone, representing that I have traveled four miles.

Ranger Beads

By the end of the training, I felt confident that I could navigate blindly through the desert as long as I had my map, compass, and ranger beads. Jason helped those of us militia members who didn't have ranger beads make our own.

The next training session was scheduled for after lunch, which was included with the $20 donation Paul had asked everyone to chip in. Simple: hot dogs and hamburgers with chips. It was tasty to me. During lunch I overheard a few of the KLC guys talking with Jason.

"Paul... did you bring the pyrotechnics with you?" Jason asked, then took a bite of his burger.

Paul laughed off his question and kept flipping burgers, shaking his head.

"Come on, Paul ... Did you bring the good stuff this time?" Jason asked again.

"No. We don't do that stuff, Jason," Paul said, looking around to see who was within earshot.

"We're out of the C business now?" Mike asked, but I didn't know what he was talking about. The conversation was quickly shut down as

Tom and I sat down. *C business?* I thought. They might have been referring to C4, the explosive, but it was a wild ass guess.

After lunch we were back at it again. This time Jason was teaching patrol tactics. I knew police patrol tactics, but not military-style desert patrol tactics. Jason went over what a typical militia patrol squad looked like, but also threw out the disclaimer that it was up to each unit's commander how he wanted to equip, name, and stack his patrol teams.

- Point Man – PT
- Rifleman – RM
- Patrol Leader – PL
- Assistant Patrol Leader – APL
- Grenadier – AG
- Radio – RTO
- Automatic Weapons – AW
- Rear Guard – RG

We separated into different squads and Jason walked us through each patrol position and their duties. He then moved on to how to set security along with different patrol formations, including the wedge, staggered column, inverted wedge, and the line.

As a police officer it was mind-blowing to me that here was a former Army Ranger training everyday citizens in military tactics to rise up against its own government. Could that be true? Or were they just gun *enthusiasts* like I read in some newspapers or some claimed to be? *Enthusiasts of what?* I pondered. The training was basic and boring for me but I was trying to act not too comfortable with the movements Jason was teaching. After a couple hours of movement training, we took a break and huddled under several sun shades at base camp transitioning into administrative topics.

MML Machine

First up was a militia man named Ryan from the KLC group. Ryan was dressed in desert camo fatigues and wearing decent boots that looked extremely comfortable to me on this hard, rocky desert ground. Long straggly hair, thinner than I would expect for his age, falling in the 35 to 40 range. Cursed with a bad complexion, his face was pitted and blotchy, I'm not certain if it was from a previous drug addiction or just bad genes. It looked like he had tattoo sleeves on both arms but his jacket covered them.

"What's up, guys! Thanks for coming out and great training, Jason!" Ryan said to the group now encircled around him. His voice shocked me. He was articulate and enthusiastic with his tone. Not what I was expecting based on his appearance and mannerisms. Ryan had a contraption in front of him. Think about the machine that Will Smith was selling at the beginning of the movie *The Pursuit of Happyness*, even though this was a decade before that movie was released.

"My fellow militia brothers…" Ryan said and went on to claim that his machine could cure most major diseases that the government claimed were incurable. "The government has the cure for cancer but refuses to admit it to the public because of the drug companies and the money involved." Ryan said that when he presented his research and findings about his machine to the government they had attempted to assassinate

124

him. His response had been to fight the government and go underground with the militias. He was now the head medical scientist for the militias of the western region. Ryan went on to demonstrate the machine which he called the MML, but for the life of me I cannot remember what the heck that stands for. Miracle Machine Love?

Ryan began to demonstrate the machine, hooking up what looked like four leads extending from the machine to the body. He said that the machine sent electromagnetic pulses to the body to break up the *bad cells, disease, etc.* so the human body can dispose of its contents. It would cure wounds, bones, cancer, and AIDS.

"Who wants to try it?" Ryan said after his lecture.

Guess who volunteered to get hooked up to this crazy contraption in the middle of nowhere? For those of you who were thinking it was me, that would be an *absolutely not!*

David, the crazy black man, jumped up. "Hook me up. I want to try it."

Ryan had him hooked up within a couple of minutes and it looked like it was shocking the hell out of him, but David didn't seem to mind. I was hoping Ryan would hook it up to his head or maybe his ball sack. People were fascinated by this machine and at least four people said they wanted to buy one for the $300 sales price.

We broke for free time followed by dinner. Pork and beans. It was going to be a gassy night for me. Shockingly, I never saw even one ounce of alcohol or drugs. Was I the only one that wanted an ice-cold beer?

Russian Troops Operating in the United States

Joel, the commander of the KLC, kicked off the next topic with more thankyous and welcomes. The next topic was a discussion about the Russian troops training on United States soil. The Cold War had officially ended about five years prior, but the militias believed that our government was trying to abolish the constitution of the United States in favor of a *One World Government*. Why else would we ever let the Russian troops train on United States soil? The group was fired up! The Commander passed around what looked like surveillance photos of the Russian troops training as proof. Were the photos real? No idea. What do I know about the Russian military? Nothing! The group talked about this one topic for approximately one hour before moving onto the next.

Security Update

Dean, the head of security, addressed the group next.

"Countrymen. We're under attack. The government knows that we're onto their game and that we're willing to die to protect our Sovereign Nation. That comes at a price as you know. That's why we're out here. Training and getting prepared for a fight that we know is going to come. It may be here sooner than we once thought! We have had two of our members here today that have caught the government going through their trashcans at their houses!" Dean's chest flared. I could tell he was pissed. "I want you to hear it from them so you know that it is accurate and truthful," Dean continued. "Tom or Paul? Who wants to go first?"

Dean took a seat back in his camping chair, sporting a captain's rank insignia on it. Paul stepped forward.

"To be clear. I did not see it personally, but my neighbor did. He said that he saw a car pull up to my house with two guys. The trunk of the vehicle was open and the passenger jumped out of the car and threw my trash into the trunk and then they drove away. He didn't get a good look at either guy and he wasn't sure what kind of car it was. That's all I know but I believe him," Paul said.

Tom stood up next to Paul. "Well, I did see the guy who took my trash and he was definitely a government agent. Same thing happened to me. A car pulled up real early in the morning. It was still dark out. The trunk was open and the passenger got out to get my trash, but he dropped the can. I saw them. So, I went to go get my gun to confront them, but they were gone by the time I got back. He didn't get all of my trash. The car looked maybe brown and had four doors but I'm not sure of the make or model," Tom said. "The government is always watching you. I am proof. I'm just renting a room. How did the government know where I lived? Nothing of mine is public. I don't even get mail at my place."

I knew then. I was responsible for all of this. The trash runs had to be Al and Mick's crew. I knew they'd followed Tom to his place a long time ago and got his address but I didn't know about the trash runs. The information flow was a one-way street. I never knew what was going on with the investigation or what my handlers were up to. My hands began to sweat and my heart rate quickened. I knew this feeling and it hadn't had a good outcome last time.

"Could there be a rat?" Ralph asked, looking around at the group. I mirrored his movements.

"Good point and funny you should say that," Dean chimed in. "For the safety of everyone, the militias, and our mission, we're going to search everyone and all of your stuff. Your commanders already agreed. It's nothing personal and it's for the safety of the *movement*. Before we start, I want to read the following statement." Dean pulled out a paper and began to read:

"Agent Provocateur – As an agent of the government, either foreign or domestic, in an official or unofficial capacity, law enforcement, federal, state or local, you must identify yourself when asked. If you are any of these I ask you now to identify yourself and surrender yourself to this militia. Safe quarters will be provided to you."

Everyone was looking around at each other to see if anyone was going to step forward. No one did.

"Okay. Everyone stay here until you are called. I, along with your commander, will search your person, vehicle, and camp together. You will

128

be present during any and all searches. Anything found outside of agent provocateur evidence will be kept confidential. Does anyone have any objections?" Dean asked.

"You can search my shit. As long as I get to search your shit too. Jason, you knew and didn't tell us? That's fucked up man," David said.

Dean agreed to David's terms. "Well let's go then bitch," David said to Dean and tensions were high. Everyone just sat in the dirt waiting for their name to be called. I wasn't worried about them searching me or my stuff. I knew that I was clean, but I was worried about someone planting something in my stuff. David returned even more pissed.

"These fuckers don't know how to find a snitch. If there is a snitch I could find them," he said to the group as he sat back down in the dirt. I could tell he was about ready to lose his shit. The Denali Park militia was clear and our Rainier Park militia group was next. I volunteered to go first since I had the least amount of stuff, but I did have a vehicle. They searched me, my duffle bag, sleeping bag, and vehicle. Checked my car registration, under the seats, trunk. I give the search a 9 out of 10.

"Sorry, Steven," Tom said to me.

"I don't know the right answer here, Tom. I get it, but this will set the trust back within our units. There had to be a better way," I said.

When I was walking back to my dirt seat I saw David in Ryan's face.

"Are you the snitch?" David said as he poked him in the chest.

Ryan didn't engage and David went back to his seat still stewing. I tried not to make eye contact with his crazy eyes, but I saw him out of my peripheral get up and walk in my direction. I didn't want to get into it with

David, so I headed back over to Tom and Dean who were now searching Jeff's stuff.

"Hey Dean or Tom. My stuff has been searched and I have to go to the bathroom. Is it cool if I take a leak right over there?" I asked.

"Yeah, that's fine, Steven, but then make sure you go right back, to be fair to the group," Tom said.

"Of course," I said, hoping by the time I got back David's craziness would have subsided.

I finished my business and headed back to the circle. I didn't see David as I got closer. Thank God, I thought. Next thing I knew, David had jumped on my back from behind, wrapping his legs around my waist and causing us to fall to the ground. I quickly put my chin down to safeguard my airways as his left arm reached around my neck.

"Are you a snitch?" David said with an evil laugh, but I wasn't laughing. I'm not sure what happened to me. Maybe it was because he was right. I was the snitch; defenseless in the middle of the desert, out-numbered, with no help. No badge to hide behind. No gun.

Maybe it was our past where he'd put a knife to my throat in jest. Maybe it was just because he was a bully and an asshole or a combination of all of them which I can't stand. I heard lectures and watched videos in the police academy about *the will to survive* as a cop, but never really understood it until then. My body took over and to this day I don't recall the exact chain of events. I remember seeing blood, but not feeling any pain. I remember the end of the fight. I had David wrapped up with my legs and his upper torso was controlled by a head and arm choke. I had the choke tight and was slowly sucking the life out of his body. I saw a knife to my left that had blood on it. I wanted to reach for it, but I was afraid I

130

would lose my hold on him. Still in survival mode, oblivious to everything but surviving, I continued to squeeze. His right arm I remember was flailing, hitting me, trying to get an airway. But I could tell by the force of his flails, his airway was about to close and I wasn't going to let go. Soon his body went limp.

"Break it up. Break it up. Let him go. Stop. You're going to kill him. Oh, fuck there's blood. Did he stab him?" All things that I heard, but I have no idea who said them or when. Ralph told me later that he, Jonny and Mike tried to break it up, but they couldn't get me to let go. Now here is where some freaky stuff comes into the story. I was not a muscular guy by any means, but on that day I had the strength of Goliath. David's body was limp, but I had not released my hold. "*Let him live*," I heard. A calmness came across my body that I had never felt before and my grip on David's throat released. Pushing David's limp body away from me, I realized that the back of my right hand had been slashed and was leaking blood. Knife cuts always bleed a lot. Ralph helped me up, wrapping my hand with what I believe was one of his shirts.

"Fuck, man. Are you okay? You're bleeding pretty bad. Are you cut anywhere else?" Ralph asked me.

"David. David. Wake up!" I heard someone yelling.

"I think he's dead. He ain't moving," someone else said.

"Does he have a pulse?" someone asked.

"He ain't dead. Get out of my way. Put him on his back. Johnny, hold his feet up in the air," Jason said as he took over. Tom took me away from the bloody scene and over to his truck, pulling out a first aid kit.

"What happened?" Tom asked as he went through his first aid kit.

"He jumped on me calling me a snitch and he had a knife," I said.

131

"What?" Tom asked. "Damn, dude, you're cut pretty good. You're going to need stiches. Let's see if these butterflies will hold it. I have to clean it first and this is going to hurt," he said. I could tell that Tom hadn't been around much blood before nor been exposed to the darker side of this life. The waterfall of hydrogen peroxide and pain that followed is burned more into my brain than the actual fight. Just so everyone knows: hydrogen peroxide has fallen out of grace to clean wounds. Use water with a mild soap.

The life in David began to stir again and before everyone knew it he was back on his feet asking for me.

"Where's Steven? I was just joking, man," he said, looking for supporters.

"Hey, David's looking for you. What do you want to do?" Tom asked me.

"Fuck him. I'll go over there," I said.

"I'm going to send Jeff over here to stay with you until I get back. Let me talk to the commanders," Tom said nervously. This was uncharted territory for him and it showed.

Jeff showed up shortly and we struggled to talk, not sure whose side he'd chosen. My mind began to shift on what the Department was going to think about my actions and how they were going to handle it. Second guessing myself. What could I have done differently? Now I was going to have to worry about this motherfucker the rest of my life.

Tom approached us. "How's your hand?" he asked.

"I think it's okay. I can still move my fingers so that's good. If I can just get this to stop bleeding," I said. The knife slash stung more than it hurt.

132

"Okay. The commanders have decided to conduct an investigation. Interview everyone before they decide what to do," Tom said.

"Tom. It doesn't have to be that way. I'm good. Let's just see if David and I can work it out. If not, then you guys decide," I said.

"You're okay with doing that?" Tom asked.

"Yeah. Let's do it," I said, knowing that I wanted to stay close to David where I could keep my eye on him. I was afraid what might happen if the commanders decided they would keep us apart. David was my number one target at his point.

Tom walked me over to where David was sitting. It looked like he had two sentries guarding him or like he was under arrest.

David stood up when he saw me walking towards him with extended arms. "Steven. I was just joking, man. Are you okay?" he said with a laugh, not realizing that only by the grace of God, not me, he was alive.

"I'm okay," I said, not asking or caring if he was okay.

"Are we cool?" he asked me, wanting to hug it out.

"We're cool," I said, and I gave him the non-verbal cue that he could come into my personal space. We embraced quickly, but when I felt him go to pull away I held him tight. Just briefly. Whispering, "I'll kill you if you come at me again." He nodded. I'm not sure if it was in agreement or he took it as a challenge. It didn't seem to matter to either of us. The line in the sand was drawn and we both seemed comfortable knowing our boundaries.

The group went on like nothing had happened, at least on the surface. They continued with the remaining security searches. They gave me the green light to go lie down in my tent. Kelly posted a chair outside

133

my tent as my watch guard in her mind. I appreciated the thought and dozed off for a short nap, waking up to nightfall. Kelly still sitting outside at her post.

"Hey, how do you feel?" she asked when I poked my head out. "Sorry, if I woke you. They're heading out for the night patrol training, but I didn't know if you were coming and I didn't want to leave you," she said with a pink flower in her hair tonight.

"Yeah. I'll go. When are they leaving?" I asked.

"Right now," she said.

"Can you tell them that I want to go and to give me five minutes?" I said.

"Yeah. Are you sure?" she asked and I nodded.

The last block of training for the night started and all were shocked that I was attending. The training was on night patrols. Basically, the same stuff we'd learned earlier in the day but applying it to an all-in-one exercise. The mission was to conduct a patrol and recover a pack one mile from our camp. Each squad was given a topo map marked with an X designating the location of the pack. We had to shoot an azimuth, set our course, and find the pack and then navigate back to base camp. It was dark that night and the stars weren't helping our vision. Three patrols went out that night and I was in the last group with Tom and Jason. David was in the patrol in front of me, but I tried to block him out of my mind and just stay alert. I knew they had put both Tom and Jason in my patrol for a reason, but I wasn't sure if they were worried about David getting me or me getting David. Everyone completed the challenge that night and then went off to bed or at least their little circles to talk about the day's excitement. My group was great and wanted to partake in the drama, but I deferred the best I could. I knew the more I talked about it the more trouble I could get myself in as a police officer.

"Hey Tom. I don't think it was you but whoever came up with the 'hey, maybe we have a snitch' plan is an idiot," Jeff said and I started to chuckle a bit. His timing was perfect and it was funny even though that was not his intention.

"No, it wasn't me and yes I agree. Sorry again guys," Tom said.

"Well, they know that Steven isn't a cop. He almost killed David. If it wasn't for Johnny and those guys he would be dead," Jeff said.

"I wasn't going to kill him Jeff," I said, still not sure where Jeff stood with the incident.

"Whatever you say, man. My point is you're not a cop," he said.

"I don't think any of you are cops either for whatever that's worth. I've had enough fun for one day. I'm going to go lie down," I said, leaving the group for the night. I didn't sleep much that night and I was happy to see the sunrise in the morning. The training was over the next morning and everyone said their goodbyes. David and I actually hugged it out before I left but he just made the top of my target list, in all bold capital letters.

The drive home was emotional. Thought provoking. Frightening. Enlightening. Every cop ponders it. Many wonder if they will hesitate when faced with it. Some can't do it. Some never recover from it. But one thing is for certain … all cops live with it. The *it*, taking the life of another person. As a young cop, I had pulled my weapon in the line of duty every night on patrol, but I never really came close to pulling the trigger. Our patrol car took a bullet one night but the cowardly bastard never showed his face. I had been in a few fisticuffs, but they were generally over someone not wanting to go to jail, school yard bullies, or women. Never had I felt my life was in jeopardy until David.

It's a tough mental discussion, knowing that you wanted to kill another human being. Societal machismo rationalized my desires and boasts that man would and should kill man to protect their family. Declarations of empty souls never really put to the test. God commands us: *Thou shall not murder.* I wanted to end David's existence on this earth, a problematic desire as a self-declared Christian man. Even more scary to me was that *God* was fucking real! There was no other explanation as to why David lived out that day. Growing up Methodist, deploying my Christianity card when it was convenient to me, always doubting God's existence internally but not through my words. Adam and Eve? Seriously. Science disagrees.

A large pothole in the road broke my reverie. A few miles later I understood *his* message and it was life altering. I am not allowed to *choose* who lives and who dies, period. It doesn't matter how bad the situation is or how bad the person is. If there is a *choice* of life or death it is not mine to make. If I have no choice … so be it, and God will forgive me.

Debrief

Al's turn in the barrel, unfortunately for me, but I was hoping he wouldn't want to debrief that night. He waived our meet, opting to debrief in the morning with Mick. Good news for me because I was mentally and physically exhausted. The next morning, I met Al and Mick at Al's favorite coffee shop.

"What happened to your hand? Did you cut yourself?" Mick said immediately after I got the all clear and took my seat.

"Something like that," I said.

Al still hadn't lowered his newspaper.

"What do you mean?" Mick asked.

"I got into it with David. The crazy black dude," I said, and Al lowered the newspaper.

"What do you mean you got into it?" he said, looking over his glasses resting on the bridge of his nose.

"Reader's Digest version: the KLC Commanders believed there was a snitch because a few of the guys' trash was searched. So, they did a surprise search. They searched us and all of our shit," I said as Al interrupted me.

"They believe there is a snitch and searched all of your shit?"

"Yeah. Was that you guys that got caught doing the trash searches?" I asked.

Al's face gave me the answer but he never admitted it.

"Yeah. They searched me and all of my crap. But just not me. They searched everyone," I said.

"No shit! Fuck me," Mick said.

"Did they find anything on you?" Al asked.

"No. Of course not," I said.

"How did you get into it with David?" Mick asked and I could tell Al's wheels were spinning.

"David flipped. He was pissed and started getting in people's faces trying to find the snitch," I said as Al interrupted me again.

"So, you get in a fight with the guy. Fuck. You're done. You just blew up this whole assignment!"

"Hey, wait a minute, Al. We don't know that," Mick said. A feeble attempt to calm Al.

"Al. It wasn't like that, man! I walked away knowing this crazy fucker was going to get in my face. When I came back this guy jumped on my back with a knife to my throat calling me a snitch. What was I supposed to do?" I asked.

"So, he knows you're a snitch. I knew it. We're done," Al said.

"No. He doesn't know shit. He was calling everyone a snitch. If anything, I am the last person they believe is a snitch now," I said, trying to make my point.

"Al, wait, man. Let's just hear the whole story," Mick said.

"That's it, man. I got him off me and my hand got cut somewhere along the way," I said.

"Did he try to kill you?" Mick asked.

"Not sure. He said he was just fucking around but it didn't feel like it and I didn't wait to find out," I said.

"Did you kill the guy?" Al asked with a dramatic pause.

"Nope," I said.

"Okay. Okay. Let's back up," Mick said. "Where are you hurt and is he hurt?"

"My hand is cut and that's it," I said.

"How bad is it? Do you need stitches?" Mick asked.

"No. Tom had a first aid kit and we got the bleeding stopped and Jason superglued it," I said.

"Jason superglued your knife cut?" Al said.

138

"Yeah," I said, knowing what was coming next.

"Are you fucking stupid?" Al asked. "I don't even know how to write that up. You're fucking unbelievable."

"Al. It's fine. We'll deal with it. What about David?" Mick asked.

"He's fine. I choked him out and he had a few scrapes, but that's it," I said.

"You choked David out! Ahhh fuck!" Al said as Mick chuckled, kicking me under the table.

"That's the same as deadly force on the use of force scale. We have to report all this," Al said, thinking out loud. "You might as well have shot him. It would have been cleaner than this."

"I didn't have a gun or I would have," I said sarcastically.

"What fucking *bird* gets into a deadly use of force?" Al said, continuing to think out loud, not caring or realizing I could hear the conversation he was having with himself.

The debrief lasted forever and Al sent me home suspending my undercover duties until further notice. I wasn't sure if I was happy, sad or pissed that my undercover assignment was up in the air. Those emotions turned to anger quickly. I didn't want things to end this way but I felt at least Al did even though I didn't have any proof of that. I knew Mick would try and salvage my assignment but he was new to the division and I didn't know how much *juice* he had. The next day I got a call from Al telling me it was business as usual with no further explanation.

Hell Week

Undercover Style

"I work the way a cow grazes."

Käthe Kollwitz

Unintentionally, the 'David' incident elevated my status within the militia community. Word spread quickly and the story continually evolved until it was more legendary than truthful. In one rendition I heard weeks later, I sounded like Goliath or Jason Bourne; you know the plot. Jason Bourne would be my pick, I think! Every non-snowflake man wants to be Jason Bourne at some point in his life. David was viewed as a loudmouth wingnut who could damage the reputation of the movement by his stupidity or 5150 mental state. I'm not sure which is more relevant. Another ancillary benefit I received was a virtual get out of jail free card similar to my favorite board game *Monopoly*. But different. In this case, I received an *I'm not a cop virtual pass*, at least temporarily. Having a pass coupled with a new elevated status as a doer vaulted my access to groups and intelligence within the militia ranks. I was trusted…

Sunday

The following week, an unusually hot day with fall nowhere in sight, but it was a great day to have a little girl's birthday party by the pool, any mom would agree. Approximately fifty friends and family of Rochelle's showed up for Sophia's birthday party. There weren't any decorations, surprise clown appearances, jumpers, video game trucks, but there was a piñata, lots of food, drinks, music and dancing. I arrived late to the party even though I lived about a hundred yards away. Not to my surprise, I was the only white person in attendance and most likely invited.

"Look, *Boo*. Steven is here," Rochelle said.

Sophia saw me and ran to jump into my arms for her hug like she was accustomed to doing. Adorable. Floral white and pink dress, white shiny shoes and her hair was in braided pig tails which was generally only done for Sunday mass.

"Hi, you must be Steven. We've heard a lot about you. I'm Sophia's *Tia*," a lady said to me after I let Sophia down.

"Hi, you must be Steven. I'm Sophia's other *Tia*. Would you like me to fix you a plate?" she said. I went on to meet at least three more *Tias*, I believe, but they all looked similar to me. I didn't have any intention of staying at the party, but the food was fantastic and I missed the family time feel. I loved every minute of it. The food, the music, the beer was ice cold and of course the traditional Mexican dancing. White people are so *vanilla* with our traditions. Could that be the real reason we've been given the label *white* and not due to our skin color? Mexicans, this was before Americans were so offended by labels or words, sure know how to party and are so carefree. Why are *white* people so proper, I thought? The piñata was my favorite part. There's nothing like watching a child's face right before striking a piñata. Standing in line waiting their turn. Similar to race horses loading at the starting gate of the Preakness. Waiting intently and extremely focused for just one piece of candy to spill from the piñata. Then boom! They're off to the races for that one piece of candy that's fallen to the ground. The anxiousness of being blindfolded and not wanting to miss the piñata in front of all of their friends. The determination and desire shown by the wild swings of the stick with no real plan. The jubilation when they feel and hear the thump of success. Gathering and enjoying the fruits of victory as the piñata's guts are revealed, dumping the candy onto the ground. So pure.

One too many drinks over my social gathering threshold, I was approached by Rochelle's friend Jessica. "So, Steven, what's up with you and Rochelle? She said *nothing* – is that true?" she asked.

"Rochelle is great. I love her and Sophia, but it's not like you're thinking. We're just friends," I said.

"Okay, that's fine. But she thinks the world of you. You know that, right?" she said.

"I think the world of her too, Jessica. She's good people," I confirmed.

"Be careful. You know Sophia has told people that you're her dad?" Jessica told me in confidence.

"Ahhhh. That's really cool, but I'm not trying to be her dad. I just watch her every now and then when Rochelle needs me to. We just play games, but I'm not trying to be her dad," I reiterated.

"I know. But she really doesn't see her real dad much," Jessica explained.

"Yeah, I knew that, I've never met the guy either. It's none of my business. We just help each other out from time to time," I said.

"No worries. Well, thank you for helping my sister out," Jessica said, giving me a hug in a sincere welcoming way.

"Anytime. She's the best," I said.

"Steven, you and my sis should think about a *friend with benefits* relationship because that girl needs to get laid," she boldly said.

I chuckled, a little caught off guard by her bluntness. "Okay, I'll keep that in mind, Jessica."

It was getting late and I had stayed way longer than I expected, eaten too much food and drunk a little too much alcohol. Time for me to leave. *Let me say goodbye to the girls before I sneak out of here*, I thought.

"Steven, before you leave we have to get a picture of you and Sophia," Rochelle said. I agreed, not thinking too much about it until after the fact. Dang it! Why did I do that? It was against my op sec protocols to be photographed as Steven. What a dumb ass. Too much alcohol and I let my guard down. I needed to get out of there before I screwed anything else up. I left quickly, still pondering my photographic blunder when I came across a man I didn't recognize sitting on the top step just outside my apartment.

"Hey? Can I squeeze by you?" I asked, which seemed to startle or awaken the man, causing him to lift his head. We locked eyes. I knew and he knew without a formal introduction that he was Sophia's dad. I was uncertain about his level of angst against me since we had never met and I didn't know anything about him. His level of angst was quickly revealed as he lunged toward me; technically I'm going to say he missed. Unfortunately, I also lost my footing and fell down the stairs.

"Fuck you, white boy! I'm her daddy!" the man yelled at me as I was lying at the bottom of the stairs trying to figure out if I was hurt, but alcohol was my friend. The man, a small, skinny, wiry Mexican dude, wearing the fashionable wife beater white tank top, was heading down the stairs in my direction. It was like slow motion for me. I'm not sure if it was my graceful fall down the flight of stairs or if it was the four Coronas I'd drunk, but regardless, I was not on top of my game.

Next thing I knew, the skinny, wiry Mexican dude got clocked in the face by Rochelle's brother, Luis, before he reached me. A younger, larger man who I hadn't talked to at the party, but I did remember admiring his tattoo on his right shoulder/bicep. It was more like a mural, which will give you an indication of the enormity of his biceps.

"Fuck you, Rafino! You were told not to come here, bitch," Luis yelled at Rafino who was now lying next to me, *leaking* from his nose.

Rafino made the mistake of trying to get up, only to be met by Luis's fist a second time, this time more violently.

"That's right. Get up again, you little bitch. I told you if you come around my sister again I was going to fuck you up," Luis yelled as he punched Rafino in his lifeless face. "Motherfucker." Luis gave him a front kick to the stomach before walking away.

"Steven, are you okay? Are you bleeding?" Rochelle said to me, seeming concerned; no one seemed to care about the wiry Mexican dude, unconsciously leaking next to me.

"Yeah. I'm okay. I think that's his blood. He didn't hit me. I fell down the stairs," I said, but I don't think anyone believed me as sirens soon echoed in the background. As the sirens grew nearer, the crowds began to disappear, just like I remembered back in patrol after we responded to a homicide. My instinct was to stay, call 911 and render aid to this man. Even though he'd intended to hurt me. But I didn't. I went upstairs to the safety of my apartment and let someone else deal with the leakage.

Once inside, I thought, *Man, what a great party, except for the ending. Thank goodness Sophia didn't see any of the adult drama.*

Twenty minutes later. *Knock, knock, knock…* I heard the police radio traffic outside my door.

"Police." *Knock, knock, knock.*

145

"Police." Panicked and feeling like a criminal, fear took over and I didn't answer the door. I wasn't sure what to do, but the officers were very persistent and seemed to know that I was inside.

"Hi, Officer," I said after opening the door.

"Can we come in and talk to you for a minute?" said Officer Jones, who was a two striper, training officer. A semi-timid, slick-sleeve, female officer stood off to the side. Instantly, I could tell she was a *boot*.

"Sure." I stepped aside, welcoming the officers inside my apartment. Valley Division Patrol. The boot's name badge came into my view along with her badge number. Mendoza – 15000 series badge. Based on her badge number, we had to have been on the academy grounds at the same time, just not the same class, but I didn't recognize her.

"Is there anyone else in the apartment?" Officer Jones asked me.

"No, sir," I said.

"Do you mind if we check? It's for officer safety reasons," Jones asked. A standard line that was drilled into my head in the academy to rationalize an unarticulated legal search of one's person or residence. It sounded like complete bullshit from the other side of the street.

"No. sir. Go ahead," I said.

The boot walked into my room cautiously with her right hand on her gun. I heard my closet door open. "Clear, sir," she called out in a robotic voice that I had done a hundred times in the past, not realizing how ridiculous it sounded in this setting. *A little overkill*, I thought. *I'm the victim here and you're clearing my one-bedroom apartment with your hand on your gun? Someone please tell this boot that she's working the Valley and not the south end. This girl thinks she's a gunslinger in the south.*

"Sir. Are you hurt? Do you need an ambulance?" Officer Jones asked me.

"No. I'm fine," I said instinctually, realizing I'd just admitted some involvement without trying. Officer Jones gave a *metro nod* to the boot, indicating she needed to take point on this call.

The boot followed Officer Jones's cue. "What's your name and DOB?" she asked in the same robotic voice, standing in an aggressive interview stance with her gun leg back. Knowing that I was going down a path of no return, I wanted to minimize my exposure to any official police records as Steven. So I decided to use *The Tori*.

The Tori – a woman that I worked with at a department store while attending college. Much older than I was at the time and she was a department head. Attractive, energetic, and confusingly friendly to me. I'm not sure she would earn the "cougar" title in today's terms because we never really dated. A true mystery woman. She seemed to always have the upper hand on the conversation with me no matter what I would do. Every time I would try and get a straight answer out of her she would muddy the water by asking me a question about my question. It was confusing but effective, never giving me a straight answer. The Tori was born. I refined this technique during my undercover assignment and used it often as an avoidance technique.

#1 Ask a question about the question.

#2 Ask for more information about the question.

#3 Compliment, followed by a pivot question about an unrelated topic.

#4 Repeat.

"Sir, can you tell me what happened?" the boot asked me.

"I was hoping you could tell me?" I said.

"Sir? You don't know what happened?" the boot asked, puzzled by my question.

"No. I was hoping you guys could tell me? Is everything okay?" I asked.

"Yes. We got a call of a 415 fight and were told that you were involved?" the boot answered.

"What does a 415 fight mean?"

"Oh sorry, sir. That's just means a disturbance or fight," the boot responded.

"What kind of fight is a 415?" I asked.

"It's nothing, sir. It just means there is a fight in progress," she said, remaining in her robotic on-guard voice.

"Oh. Okay. Thank you for your service by the way. You look young. Is it hard to be a cop?" I asked.

"Yes, sir. But I love my job. You should do it. We're hiring I believe," she said in a softened voice, breaking character slightly.

"Great, thank you. That's very cool. How long have you been a cop?" I asked.

Officer Jones interrupted my questioning. "Sir. I've never seen you around here before. Have you lived here long?" he asked, done with my games.

Officer Jones was leaning up against my doorway watching the show, not concerned about his gun leg stance or an ambush around the corner of my one-bedroom apartment. A noticeably tenured officer, but not by his physical attributes, salt and pepper hair, with a matching bushy mustache, weathered steely eyes, fit, tailored uniform extra tight around the

148

bicep area, spit-shined boots, paint-worn PR-24 or broken-in gun leather, but it was his mannerisms that gave it away. Confident, but humanizing. He saw me for who I was. He knew instantly that I was involved in the call and asked if I needed medical attention. He understood that I was the only white guy in the entire apartment complex and that there was no way I was going to give up any information on my neighbor's ex-baby daddy, who'd got his ass kicked by her little brother and that street justice was most likely already served; case closed. Similar to captains on sports teams or bullies on a playground back in my day: if you got out of line or too far outside the norm, expect to get regulated. Unlike today, where street justice is persecuted. Political. Not popular. Teachers are forced and encouraged to teach children to express themselves in ways their frontal lobe is not developed enough to even understand. News and social media paint a glorious picture of socialism. Equal rights for all when they spit on and burn the very thing that symbolizes those rights. Where life is fair. Doesn't happen behind the scenes and it never will. Hard work was meant to be rewarded. Rules were meant to be followed. Consequences are a real thing. People's work ethic, character and ideologies will never be the same. Not everyone should be rewarded the same.

"Hey Steven, here is our information. The report number is on the back. If you change your mind or remember anything don't hesitate to give us a call," Officer Jones said and gave the boot another metro nod, signaling they were clearing. That was it. Just like that. The officers left.

Monday

"Steven, report to the office. Steven, report to the office," echoed across the speakers of the department store, making a statement to the other department heads that I was in trouble. That couldn't be good, I thought to myself and wondered what had happened while I'd been gone over the weekend.

"Hey, Steven. I'll keep this short. I see that you took more time off. You are the department head and we give you a ton of flexibility but you have been taking too much time off and your sales are dropping. Your department is the focused sale for this month's ad and I need to know that you have this under control. Are we clear?" Dan, the store manager asked me in a no bullshit manner.

"Yes sir. I understand. I'm sorry," I said, not offering any explanation.

"Great. Glad we understand each other," Dan said, now preoccupied with the next task on his list. I wonder what mine said? Chew Steven's ass?

Everyone was coming up to me as I walked back to my department asking what Dan had got me for. "Code X, Sporting goods," I heard come across my hand-held radio clipped to my trouser pocket. *It's going to be one of those days*, I thought to myself but I ignored the code X and continued to my electronics department.

"Hey boss, didn't you hear the code X in sporting goods?" Salvador asked as he passed me with a fast-paced walk.

"I did... all you today, Sal," I said, shaking my head at the adolescent games men play. Code X was a secret code between me,

Salvador, Oz and Nester. Whenever one of us saw an attractive woman in the store, we would call out Code X over the radio and the department she was in. It was bro code at its finest. Misogynist in today's terms and likely disqualifying me from any political aspirations I might have in my later years. I passed on this one. I was already on Dan's naughty list.

I returned to my department to get back to work, with only a few days left to prepare for our big electronics sale.

"Excuse me. Can you help me?" I heard a female voice call out from behind me. I closed my eyes as I shook my head slightly left to right in denial. *Why today?* I thought to myself before I turned around. Her voice was easily recognizable. The perfume smell confirmed my suspicions.

There she was standing at the electronics counter at my work with Sal and Nester peering at her from a close distance. "You didn't find what you were looking for in sporting goods?" I asked her as I turned around.

"You saw me in sporting goods? I didn't see you. That's pretty good," she said.

"What are you doing here, Sam? Today is not a good day for a surprise visit," I said.

Leaning forward she said softly, "But I'm here as a customer. I'm in need of assistance with electronics."

I hadn't seen Sam in a few months. Dressed to the nines as always: short black skirt, tight fitting black shirt accenting her breasts, covered with a black jacket but open in the front, topped off with black high heels. She warranted the Code X call-out, but was sort of overdressed for an outing at a department store in the ghetto.

"Seriously, why are you here?" I asked.

"I just wanted to check on you. Do you actually know anything about electronics?" she asked.

"I actually do, but I don't have much time today for your games," I said out of frustration.

"I have an electronic toy that's broken and he's my favorite. Do you think you could fix it?" she asked in her seductive way.

I couldn't help but laugh. Sam took my cue that I was short on time.

"Let me know when you have time to take a look at it," she said as she walked away. The saunter walk was a treat.

Immediately, Sal swooped into her spot near the counter, "Boss. Do you know her?"

"No idea Sal," I said.

"Really? She acted like she knew you."

"Nope, but I wouldn't mind finding out some day," I said.

"What? So, you do or don't know her?" he asked, still watching her walk away down the aisle towards the front of the store.

"Careful, Sal. She's gonna turn around and look back to see who is watching her before she makes the turn," I said as I left to get back to work.

"Boss, she did it! She did it! She turned around! How the fuck did you know that?" Sal asked. "You do know her, you bastard. Did you hit that?"

"Lucky guess, my friend. Lucky guess," I said with a smile.

"Hit what? Who hit what?" Nester asked, late to the game as always.

Tuesday

I woke to the sound of a loud knock at my door. The sun hadn't crested onto my nightstand yet, so it must be before 6 AM, I thought.

"Steven. It's Rochelle," I heard, knowing that bad news most likely waited behind my front door.

Knock, knock, knock… "Steven. It's me. Are you awake?" Rochelle continued.

"Yeah. Coming," I yelled back, throwing on some pants.

"Steven. Someone broke into a bunch of cars last night and yours is one of them."

I immediately thought it was her baby daddy who'd come back for some vengeance.

"Mary said she already called the police and they're on the way," Rochelle said in an excited accented tone.

She and I headed down to the car ports as she continued to vent on our travels. "They took Sophia's diaper bag and stroller. Who takes a child's diaper bag and stroller? My window is smashed and there is glass everywhere. How much do windows cost? Do you have any idea?" she asked as the bank of cars parked under the car ports came into view. Glass shards speckled the outline of each car's passenger side.

My passenger window was smashed just like the others. I didn't see a rock or any tool marks. My guess was the burglar used a punch. It's quick and effective. Nothing had been taken from my car except some loose change that I kept in the center console. My mind transferred from baby daddy to a militia member as suspect no. 1. However, that thought quickly left my mind when I saw the volume of vehicles that were victims.

A cardboard and duct tape professional had both vehicles cleaned and patched in about an hour. No bother waiting for the police to show up; I hear LAPD's response time is terrible.

Work was busy that day. I was shorthanded when my pager went off with an hour left in my shift.

Beep, beep, beep... 930-3333. A rare page from Al. Even more rare, a code three.

"Hey Al. What's up," I said, signaling to a line of customers I would be right with them.

"Hey. Your father called. He said you need to call him but he wouldn't tell me why," Al said.

"What do you mean he wouldn't tell you why?" I asked.

"He said it was personal. Actually, he told me it was none of my business but to have you call him. When I pressed him for a reason, he threatened to call the Chief if I didn't stop asking questions and get you on the phone," Al said.

That didn't seem right. *Something must be wrong*, I thought to myself.

"Excuse me, is there someone else that can help us!" a customer yelled.

Blowing her request off, I dialed my father.

"Pops?" I said when he answered the phone.

"Hey son. What's going on? How's everything with you?" he asked, but I knew.

"What is it? What's wrong?" I asked. He never really was any good at small talk. "Just tell me," I said.

"It's your grandmother, son. She's not doing well and they're not giving her much time to live. She asked for you," he said, holding his emotions back.

"She's still alive?" I asked. My eyes uncontrollably filled up with tears.

"Yes," he said, not wanting to expand.

"Where is she at?" I asked.

"San Antonio," he said.

"Tell her I'm coming," I said, hanging up the phone. The customer witnessing my heart crack before her eyes.

"Are you okay, Hun?" she asked, changing her tone.

I nodded, my speech failing me. Thinking of nothing but my Grandmother.

"Hey Al. I have to transition tonight. My grandmother is in the hospital and I'm not sure if she's going to make it," I said.

"I don't know if they can transition you right now. They're not in the office and I don't know where your stuff is at. Don't you have a meeting tonight?" Al said, thinking out loud as always.

"Al. I'm going. I don't need my stuff," I said. Knowing that he wasn't going to stop me. He just didn't know it yet.

"You can't leave without switching your identifications out. It will be a crossover," Al said.

"Al, I need you to work with me here. How can I do this? But it has to be quick," I pleaded.

"I know. Let me make a call," he said.

Ten minutes later he called me back. "Danny said he could meet you at 1800 hours for a transition," he said.

That was four hours away and I wasn't going to wait.

"Hey, Al. I called my dad back and he said it would be fine if I wait until morning. Can you have Danny meet me in the morning?" I asked.

"Yeah. Absolutely. He can. I'll make sure of it," Al said.

"Great thank you. That will work," I said, hanging up the phone.

I punched out of work and off I went to see my grandmother. Al didn't get it that I was going with or without his permission. MacGregors will always come when called. My solution: remove Al from the equation. An hour later, I was where I was supposed to be, holding my grandmother's hand at her bedside. I stayed at her bedside until they kicked me out, blowing off my militia meeting, violating protocol, lying to a supervisor. I never told Al and he never asked.

Wednesday

No sleep. Grandmother top of my mind occupying my headspace. Pondering death always slows down life and makes you think about your choices. Both of my lives were in shambles and I once again questioned my choices, my mission and the Department's commitment to this investigation.

It was a three-snooze alarm day before I dragged my butt out of bed, skipping breakfast to avoid the dreaded late mark on my timecard. I moved pallets of merchandise all day in preparation of the big electronics sale. Televisions were very heavy back in the day! I was abnormally exhausted at the end of my shift and looking forward to a nap on the couch before my meeting. I just didn't feel right. What balance I had obtained in everyday life was upset.

Joint Meeting

The Denali and Rainier Park militias held a joint meeting at Jason's house in the Valley. Attendance was strong, not leaving much room in the mid-sized home. Militia men stacked the room; there was just one woman, with a white flower in her hair, tonight. Jason had stepped up his security, adding an outside motion strobe light and a camera outside his front door after the trash run debacle. Tonight's agenda was full, covering Situational Reports (sitreps) on:

- Black helicopters flying over Los Angeles
- Russian military training at Miramar in San Diego
- Gulf War Syndrome
- Liens against public officials to fund the movement

The sitreps for the black helicopters and the Russians were repeat topics and weren't prolonged. I wanted to scream to the group that the black unmarked helicopters flying around Los Angeles were not government spies tracking militia members to seize their guns. They were actually LAPD training helicopters that the city had acquired from the military for the grand price of $1 through the military acquisition program. That's why they were not marked and black. The sitrep on the Russian military declared the Russians were now training in the San Diego area with the elite American SEAL teams. A newspaper article was passed around from the *Los Angeles Times* displaying a picture of our now Russian comrades. Shocking to me and I couldn't come up with a justification in my brain for that one. New to the table, sitreps on Gulf War Syndrome and a scam to fund the movement and extort public officials by placing liens against their homes.

Jason passed out a report, declaring, "This report is proof that our American government gave our troops chemical warfare agents. Well, let's call it what it was: nerve gas before their deployment. Telling them it was a safety precaution for all the nerve agents they were going to encounter during the Gulf War. All bullshit! They literally poisoned our own troops who were defending our country. Now they suffer from Gulf War Syndrome which the government won't even recognize as real! So, our troops can't get medical benefits! This makes my blood boil..."

The audience was fired up. "We need to go to the main stream media," Johnny said and everyone agreed. A list was made of all the mainstream media outlets, both video and print back then. Social media wasn't a thing yet. There were five volunteers and three were chosen. The lists were divvied up and given to the three selected volunteers who were going to report back next meeting with their hopeful success in spreading the *truth*.

Up next was the main topic for the evening. The tension in the air was thick before Jason even began to speak.

"Okay. I want to get everyone's opinion on this. Another group that I know of has been doing this to fund their units. I met with their commander last week and I want to go over it with everyone. These public officials making policies that violate our constitutional rights get away with murder with no recourse. We now have a way to hold them accountable or make them pay. An attorney in this group used inter alia *Anderson on the Uniform Commercial Code* and *Bankers Handbook* to draw notices of lien against these public officials for their crimes. The liens

158

are legal and conform to the Uniform Commercial Code. Their township court now has an interest in a tort claim for damages incurred by the named public officials for violations of their oaths of office. These officials are paying, funding the group!" Jason said, looking around for everyone's reaction.

"Dick is first on my list! Let's do it. Fuck these politicians," David said.

"Well, if we can't shoot the, I'm in. Let's make them pay so we can get some more guns," Ralph chimed in.

"Is that legal? Can we do that?" Tom asked.

"I'm not sure but it's working for this other group," Jason said.

"Yeah, but what state is that? Not in California. They don't allow township courts here," Tom said.

"That's a great point, Tom. I don't know the answer to that. This group is in another state," Jason said. "Just for argument's purposes. Let's say it's grey legal. Who would be in favor?" he asked and several people in the group said they were in favor.

"Steven. What do you think?" Jason asked me. I knew they were going to ask me my position but I was unclear how to answer it legally or tactically as a cop. If I said *yes*, what ramifications would that have? If I said *no*, would the boys think that I wasn't down for the cause?

"My vote would be no," I said.

"No? Why are you a no?" Johnny asked.

"I don't know enough about it to give a yes," I said.

"What do you want to know to make your decision?"

"Not sure. I'm not an attorney. That's not my thing, man. I don't know anything about liens and I don't even know what a tort is," I said.

"I agree with Steven. We have to be smart about these things. We aren't prepared or trained enough in this legal crap. Imagine if we fuck up and now the Feds are knocking at our front door using our stupid lien play to get our guns. That's just stupid," Jeff said.

"I'm not saying don't do it. I'm just saying that's not my thing. You're asking the wrong guy for legal stuff," I clarified.

"Does anyone know an attorney that could give us some advice?" Tom asked.

"I know a guy that does constitutional law. He's a patriot and I trust him," Harold said.

"Let's do that. Harold, can you get an answer by next week?" Jason asked.

"Not sure, but I'll let everyone know next meeting. If we can. This mayor needs to be first on our list!" Harold said.

"No! No! No! My councilman is first. He's such a snowflake," Mike said.

The meeting adjourned after forty-five minutes of more arguing about which public officials were going to make their target list and the pecking order of their targets. About half of us left the meeting and the others stuck around to banter, soapbox, and grab ass. A bone-crushing headache made the decision for me. I left, knowing the militia had just established a hitlist on public officials throughout the city, including the Chief of Police and the mayor. How was ATD going to handle this information? Did they have a duty to notify the public officials? If they did, my ass would be hanging out with too much exposure. These thoughts were competing with the pain in my head on my drive home.

Thursday – Granada Forum

I was slammed at work trying to get ready for my Electronic Weekend sale which was now only two days away. I changed the schedule, asking Sal to open for me, anticipating the Department's politics would be resolved by Mick and I would be moving forward with purchasing a rifle Saturday morning. I knew Dan the store manager would not be happy with my change but he wasn't there in the morning. My money was on Sal to cover me until I got back from my terrorist escapades.

"Hey, Steven. It's 6:30. I thought you were off at 5?" I heard Dan ask from down the toy aisle as he looked at his watch.

"I'm getting out of here now sir," I said in a panic, not because I was worried about Dan, but because I was supposed to meet Tom and the boys at the Granada Forum at 7. Operating with only a few hours of sleep under my belt, my stress level was extremely high trying to keep all of the balls juggling in the air.

"Did you come in later or are you on overtime?" Dan asked.

"I clocked out at 5, Dan. I'm just waiting for a friend. I'm not on the clock, sir," I said.

"Okay. But I can't have you working overtime," Dan reaffirmed.

"Sounds good, sir. I'll see you tomorrow," I said.

"I need your department to hit a homerun on this sale this weekend to hit our store goal," Dan reiterated.

"Yes, sir. My team will deliver," I reassured him.

I made a quick phone call to Mick letting him know that I wouldn't have time to meet him before the meeting.

"No problem! Call me after the meeting. Hey, Big 5 is a go!" he said in a serious tone.

"Good news. I gotta run. Talk to you later," I said, rushing out of the store.

I arrived at the Forum late again which meant that I'd be standing for the duration of the meeting. Tom made eye contact with me, mouthing an apology for not saving me a seat. Several guys I recognized from the KLC, Rainier Park and Denali Park militias were in attendance. Surprisingly, no David. I also saw three guys I assumed were Tom's new militia prospects sitting next to him.

TJ was the speaker tonight and he was speaking about Ruby Ridge, a catalyst for the militia movement. The Ruby Ridge incident occurred on August 21, 1992, a date many of the militia groups consider to be the day the militia movement was reborn. Six US Marshals went looking for Randy Weaver who had failed to show up for his court date where he was facing weapons charges. The Marshals ventured onto Mr. Weaver's land hoping to arrest him. However, Mr. Weaver's dog, Striker, started barking, alerting him to the Marshals' presence. As the story is told the Marshals began to retreat. Mr. Weaver, his 14-year-old son, Sammy and his friend, Kevin decided to investigate what the dog Striker was alerting to. Much is disputed here, but an exchange of gunfire ensued and Sammy was killed, along with Deputy Marshal Bill Degan. A stand-off ensued between the now head Law Enforcement agency in charge of the scene, the FBI, and the Weavers. The next day, an FBI sniper shot Randy Weaver when he left his home walking to the shed to check on his son's corpse. Kevin, Sammy's friend, was also shot, but survived. Unfortunately, Vicki, Randy's wife, was also shot by a sniper and did not survive.

TJ from Montana covered Ruby Ridge in detail, providing timelines, photos and commentary. It was appalling, if not shocking. Anyone in attendance at that meeting would have joined the militia. He even went a step further, doubling down by briefly covering the Waco Massacre which had occurred eight months later, ending on April 19, 1993. This time, the lead federal agency involved was the ATF, attempting to execute a similar warrant. But after another stand-off, 76 Branch Davidians perished, including 25 children. As you can imagine, the poor handling of both incidents by the FBI and the ATF was a catalyst and launching pad for the militia movement. Timothy McVeigh from the militia movement would later get payback on the government agencies by detonating a truck bomb in front of the Federal Building in Oklahoma City, symbolically on April 19, 1995, taking 168 lives.

This meeting was a militia recruiting smorgasbord filled with all different types of middle-aged men, along with a few women who hated the government and loved guns. How did we get this so wrong, I thought to myself, looking over the crowd and the magnitude of the audience. Was it my fault? TJ was a high-profile militia speaker who had traveled from Montana, not just some schmuck standing on a soapbox. I started to get pissed at myself. The mother of all militia groups was here speaking and we only had me covering this? What the fuck! There were a ton of potential and actual militia members attending this meeting and we were doing nothing. We should have had surveillance units photographing these guys and their plates to get them ID'd. How did the ATD not cover or know about this meeting?

I tried to forget about our screw up and focus on my task at hand. There had to be some other big players in attendance here. But who were they, I asked myself? That was my mission. Find one whale and get him ID'd.

Over the next hour, I studied the room. Most major players know other major players, so my strategy was to focus on who TJ was focused on. Who did TJ talk with in the breaks? Was TJ trying to conceal his relationship with anyone in the audience or downplay it?

TJ displayed a picture of Randy Weaver's son, Sammy's corpse up on the screen.

"The Marshals shot a 14-year-old boy and his dog Striker! Let me say that again. They shot a 14-year-old BOY and his dog on their own fucking land. Look at this BOY! He's dead. Then, this fucker…" TJ flipped the slides, showing the face of a man who he said was the FBI sniper that had killed Vicki, wounded the other boy and shot Randy Weaver. TJ continued, "This motherfucking coward then sniped his dad, another boy and killed his mother! This motherfucker right here did that. Your government! Sniped a mother on her own land after her son was already killed and her husband shot. Sniped another boy visiting his buddy who was already killed. Look at this motherfucker! He cowardly sniped them!" TJ continued with dramatic pauses, surveying the room which was boiling over with anger.

"What would you do if the Marshals or FBI came to your land to seize your weapons? Then killed your family!" TJ asked the crowd. "What would you do if this guy showed up on your land?" displaying a picture of the FBI sniper again.

"I know what a few guys in this room would do," TJ said, making brief eye contact with at least two guys in particular. Both of the guys TJ made eye contact with were standing and closer to the exit than I was. One

164

of the guys, a male Asian, simulated shooting the agent with his finger when his picture appeared on the screen. *He's my guy*, I thought to myself. *Let's get this guy ID'd.* But I was in the wrong position. I wanted to make my way to the other side of him so I would be in a better position without drawing too much attention to myself. Making my way towards the restroom as the meeting adjourned, it was chaos, just as I'd thought. Too many people. I couldn't move fast enough and I lost him. He was gone by the time I pushed my way through the crowds. Frustrated. Pissed. Tired. I'm not sure which adjective to choose or to add more here to best describe the way I felt and I definitely didn't want to wait for Mick to come out to meet me to rehash our missed opportunity.

But I didn't had to wait anyway. Mick drove mock two to our meet location, as always arriving in record time. I don't recall the name of the place where we met that night, but it was just off of the 405 freeway in Panorama City. We called it an *on the hood, in the hood* debrief. It was late, I remember, and I was off my game. Still pissed about our missed opportunity. Mick was great, just shaking it off and not pointing the blame, which I concluded by this time lay solely with me. I'm not sure if my memory encoding was working properly that night, but I couldn't remember anything except for TJ's speech.

"Hey, do you feel okay?" Mick asked.

"Yeah, I'm just pissed," I answered.

"You don't look good, man. Are you sure you're okay?"

"Yeah. I'm just tired. It's been a hell of a week, man and I'm trying not to screw anything up or get killed," I said.

"Hey. Let's get through this debrief so I can cut you loose. Hopefully you can get some sleep tonight," Mick said and I acquiesced to his suggestion. "I'll tell you about the SKS argument or debacle later. But bottom line is we got you the green light to buy the SKS and some ammo. Here's three hundred bucks. Buy the rifle and ammo."

"Okay, sounds good," I said, taking the cash.

"Hey. I would spend as much of those three hundred bucks as you can because it was a bitch getting that money from the Department. I just need a receipt and the change," Mick said.

"Will do. Anything else I need to do?" I asked.

"Yeah. I'll need to grab that rifle from you just for a couple of hours. I have to bring it to SID to get photographed and documented," Mick said.

"Do we have to do it on Saturday? Or can it wait for a few days?" I asked.

"No. It can wait, but just not too long or they'll have my ass. I'll do it on your time, just give me a few hours' notice so we can meet. Get out of here. It's late. Get some sleep. Hey, remember Al is covering me tomorrow night. I have a retirement party that I'm attending, but I'll pick you back up on call on Saturday."

"Sounds good. Have fun and we'll talk on Saturday sometime during the day after I get that rifle," I said as we parted ways for the night.

Friday

Five hours of sleep and I felt like a new man. It was my last day to prepare for the big electronics sale on Saturday and Sunday. I knew it was going to be a long day but the highlight of my day would be getting my window fixed. Oz had hooked me up with his homeboy Shorty again, who was coming to our work to swap it out. I was looking forward to having a glass window again. Cardboard isn't the best medium for visibility and blocking out the cold or rain. We had a cold front coming through. Well, a cold front for Southern California that is.

When I left for work that morning, I saw a car parked facing northbound on the east side of the street. I'm not sure why it caught my eye; a grey, two door sedan. Parked legally, three back from the corner. There was nothing flashy about it or distinctive. It was just a feeling I had so I decided to check it out. A feeling that before my undercover days would have never come. A feeling before my undercover days I would never have listened to.

I was traveling eastbound set up for a northbound turn. My blinker was indicating a northbound turn as I came to a stop. I saw the car to my south. I changed my direction without indication and quickly turned southbound towards the car, still parked by the curb. The turn revealed the driver. He was looking straight ahead, not in my direction. A baseball hat with a khaki shirt. My eyes were playing tricks on me because I thought I saw someone sitting in the passenger seat, but after I made the turn the passenger seat was lying flat fully reclined and I couldn't tell if someone was in the seat. I drove down to the end of the street and made a U-turn to see if I could get a plate. I saw the grey vehicle pull out and make an eastbound turn out of my view.

It was odd, but I couldn't determine if they were set up on me or someone else. Narcos? Search warrants nearby? Code Six Charles suspect? No idea, but it didn't add up to me. I dry-cleaned myself, making sure I was clear of any tails, then headed into work. I was ready for my big sale. Strange that I cared so much about my basic hourly job. I knew it wasn't my real job and it wasn't my career, but it still caused me stress and jubilation. A parent-driven trait I guess I couldn't escape.

Oz came in later that day for his closing shift and offered to help me out with any last-minute items I had. I tasked him with building a sales endcap of Kodak film, one of our hottest selling items. Cases of Kodak film filled the stock room. A product stamped irrelevant in today's digital world. Oz received a page on his personal pager and asked to use my department phone to make a call. He didn't need to ask permission but still did; we were the same rank but it was courteous. His phone call was brief but impactful.

"Yo, Whocco. I gotta bolt. Can you cover me?" he asked.

"Sure. What happened? Are you okay?" I asked.

"I'm straight. These foos just shot my cousin," Oz said. I saw the gangster awaken within him.

"Wait. What happened? Your cousin was shot? I'm sorry man. Is he okay?" I asked.

"These little poo butts don't know who they're fuckin' with. I'm going to bust a cap in someone's ass," Oz said to himself, but loud enough as he walked towards the back of the store.

"Oz. Wait up, man. Talk to me. Tell me what's going on," I said.

"I'm straight, Whocco. Just cover me ,man. You don't want to know this shit," he said, quickening his pace as I followed him upstairs to the employee lounge. Oz opened up his employee locker and grabbed a blue t-shirt that had something wrapped up inside it. I couldn't tell what it was at first, but I saw the butt of the gun as he turned away from the camera. Oz picked up the phone on the wall.

168

"Nester. We're rolling, bro. Let's go," he said as he hung up the phone and began to walk downstairs towards the front of the store.

"Oz. What the fuck? Just wait. Tell me what's going on!" I pleaded. Oz quickened his stroll.

"Whocco. It's best you don't know. We got *bidness* to handle," Oz said as he walked outside towards his car. His eyes were fixed, almost glazed over, as his anger grew. I saw the transition happening before my eyes, similar to one of my favorite TV shows back in the day; *The Incredible Hulk*. His stroll, similar to an orangutan's walk, quickened towards two guys I didn't recognize waiting in the parking lot.

The Kristy

"Oz, stop," I said, grabbing his shoulder to stop him.

"Whocco. Let fucking go of me!" he said, turning towards me. Our faces were only separated by four inches of air. His fists were cocked instinctually and we were nametag to nametag.

"I can't do it, Oz," I said.

"Get out of my way!" He shoved me backwards. His crew ran to his aid.

"Oz. I can't. You can hit me, but I can't let you go, man," I pleaded.

Two guys from his crew grabbed me and threw me to the ground before Oz called them off. They were pissed and I was scared.

"Who the fuck is this cracker?" Gangster No. 2 said, not knowing if he was supposed to punch me or help me up.

"He's Whocco. The crazy white boy that was down for Emily," Gangster No. 3 said, shaking his head. The tension eased briefly as I got off the ground, noticing that I'd ripped a hole in my new pants.

"What's your problem, Whocco?" Gangster No. 2 asked.

"I got no problems man except for ripped pants and a broken window. Did Shorty fix it today, Oz?" I asked, trying to continue to ease emotions. It didn't work, as they just stared at me like I was surely crazy.

"Seriously. I don't know what is going on, but Oz can't go," I said.

"What is this foo talking about?" Gangster No. 2 said, looking at Oz for an explanation.

"There's too many people looking at us right now. Just give it a day and let things settle down. Then figure it out." I could sense their brains processing what I was saying and I was hoping it was working. "Trust me. Nothing has to be done right now. Be smart about it," I pleaded and we heard sirens in the distance. I knew the police were coming for us.

"Fuck! I'm strapped! Are you guys strapped?" Oz asked his crew.

"They're in the car. Let's bolt," Gangster No. 2 said.

"Oz, you can't run. You work here. Don't run! Just give me the gun, Oz," I said, and he hesitated.

"Give you the gun?"

"Give me the gun and don't run," I said, looking directly into his glazed over eyes. Oz handed me the gun. A Glock. I didn't know what caliber or if it was even loaded. I tucked it in my rear waistband as the police car entered the parking lot entrance to the east.

The Paulina – A lesson I learned in training when I was completing Steven's background. The first part of the lesson was: to create a narrative

170

that you are comfortable with and that you can sell. The second part of the lesson was: sell your story first and always steer the narrative.

I waved my arms frantically at the arriving officers, signaling to them that we were in need of assistance, setting the stage for us as the victims.

"Whocco. What the fuck!" Gangster No. 2 said.

"Just shut up and be cool. Follow my lead. Don't run or say you have a car here. Oz, put your employee vest back on," I said.

The officers pulled up at a safe distance, so I approached them pointing frantically to the north.

"Hi officers. He went that way. A Mexican guy wearing black pants and a white tee shirt," I said.

"What did he do?" the first officer asked me.

"He was crouched down over there by that car. I didn't know if he was hurt or breaking into my car because it got broken into earlier. I only have cardboard on the window. I went over to him to see what was going on and he looked like he was crazy. He grabbed me and threw me to the ground then took off running," I said.

"Okay. Did he take anything or break into your car?" the officer asked me, not knowing that I had a gangster's gun in my waistband.

"No sir. I just think he was crazy."

"Who are these guys and how are they involved?" the other officer asked me, pointing to Oz and his crew.

"I work with him. He came out to help me," I said.

"Okay. So, you're okay and nothing was taken?" the other officer asked me. I could tell the officer was checking boxes to see if they could clear the call or they'd have to write *paper.*

171

"No sir," I said.

"Well. We can file a report for battery if you like and want to sign it," the officer said.

"No. I just think he was crazy. I'm not sure who called the police? I don't want to sign anything. But thank you for coming," I said.

"Show a code four. Suspect GOA and show us clear," the officer said over the radio. He handed me a business card with their information like he was supposed to do and they drove away.

"Whoa... Whocco. You're a crazy white guy. Holy shit!" Oz said.

"Let's go, Oz. You need to finish my endcap," I said.

My heart rate was still racing. Oz and I walked back into the store where we had to answer a few employee enquiries, complete a gun exchange and then back to work to finish our shift. Just another normal day in the hood it seemed. My lifestyle was setting a new *normal*. This was my third police contact this week I thought? Outside of a speeding ticket. I can only recall one prior police contact in my life. My high school girlfriend and I had gone to the park after a movie to make out – does anyone say make out anymore? Anyway, an officer shone a bright light in my truck, checked our identifications and then called her parents to let them know that their daughter was in a park with me. No fights. No guns. No gangsters. What the heck was I doing now, when this had nothing to do with my actual assignment?

Oz had one of his closers call in sick, and returning the favor I stayed a few extra hours to help him out before heading home. Besides, I was fearful he would bolt as soon as I left. I said my goodbyes and walked outside to see my car parked some distance away, lit up by the parking lot lights. Shorty had fixed it. Yes. Bye-bye cardboard window, I thought. It was a small victory, but very exciting considering my week.

I was exhausted and hadn't eaten all day, triggering my mind to wander to places I was trying to avoid. Liz, friends, family, my dog, relaxing times, my favorite restaurants and hang outs. Michael Bolton's *When a Man Loves a Woman* began to play on the radio, adding another layer of complexity to my chaotic life. I'd missed my scheduled call with Liz tonight. A call I normally looked forward to for days, counting down the hours. I'd missed it. I didn't even think about it until it was too late. It was the first time since I'd gone *under the sheets*, breaking a promise I'd made to her. How could I forget to call Liz, I thought, turning left onto Roscoe Blvd and nearing my apartment.

"Dang it! Not tonight!" I said out loud. Pissed. Realizing another surveillance car was set up outside my apartment. This car was similar but different to the car I'd seen that morning. Occupied by two silhouettes, but I couldn't make out any type of description. It was too dark. *What the hell*, I thought, committing the license plate to memory this time as I drove past them. A pile of sunflower seed shells lay just outside the driver's side door. Initiating my op sec protocols, I dry-cleaned myself. Clear. I pulled into a local 7-Eleven store to call Al, following protocol. The pay phones weren't too bad and seemed in good working condition. My call went to his voice mail. Backup plan, I paged him code three. After fifteen minutes, no luck. I repeated the process. Voicemail, a second page code three and another fifteen-minute wait period. No luck. I spotted the grey sedan from this morning pull into a parking lot across the street from me and I was down to my last set of quarters. I pivoted.

310-525-4141 …

"Hello," a chipper voice answered. It was Jules. Mick's wife.

"Hi, Jules. It's Steven. Is Mick around?" I asked.

"Oh, hi Steven. How are you? Mick went to Glynn's retirement party up at the Academy. I'm not sure what time he'll be home. Striker!" Ironically the same name as Mr. Weaver's dog, I thought. "Quit barking…" Jules continued rambling for several minutes as my eyes remained fixed on the grey sedan.

"Hey, Jules. Jules. Jules," I said repeatedly.

"Yeah. Sorry. What did you say?" she asked.

"Sorry to cut you off, but I need you to get a hold of Mick. Just tell him that I need to be *dry cleaned code three*," I said as Jules cut me off.

"Wait. What? Tell Mick to have you cleaned?" she asked.

"Jules. Listen to me. Tell Mick that I need to be *dry cleaned code three*. Trust me. He'll know what that means and write this number down: 818-787-1212. Have him call me there. Do you got it?" I asked her.

"Oh sorry. Sorry." Her voice changed immediately, not knowing what was going on but recognizing it was serious. "Okay, tell Mick that you need to be dry cleaned code three? Is that right? And have him call you at... Wait... Is it 818-787-1212?" she asked in a serious tone.

"Yes. Thanks Jules," I said.

"I'll... I'll do it right now! I promise! Bye," Jules said with panic in her voice.

Two minutes later…the pay phone rang.

"Hey Mick, sorry to bother you but I can't get a hold of Al. I think I got a tail on me," I said.

"Seriously? Is it Blue on Blue?" he asked.

174

"No idea. But that would be my guess. I don't think they're militia boys," I said.

"Did you call Al? He's covering me," Mick said.

"Yeah, I've been calling him and he didn't answer and I got this car on me," I said.

"Fucking Al. Unbelievable. Let me get ahold of G and see how to handle this. Okay. Where are you at?" he asked and I told him my location.

"Give me five minutes and I'll call you right back. Stay there," Mick said, hanging up the phone.

The phone rang two minutes later.

"Hey. I got ahold of G. He's going to meet me and we want to ID this tail. Is there a place you can go that's going to be open for a couple of hours?" he asked.

"It's late already. There's a pharmacy on Roscoe that I think is open 24 hours," I said.

"Okay. Do this. I want you to go to that pharmacy and hang out until you get a page from me. Once you get my page, get in your car and drive home. We'll counter-surveil you. If you're clean I'll page you with a code four and we'll set up on your place in the morning. We want to ID these fuckers."

"Okay. Will do," I said.

"Listen to me. When you're in the pharmacy, look for any cameras and I want you to stay in camera view at all times. Do you hear me?" he said. I could tell he was in *go mode*. "Wait for my page. Don't worry. We got you."

"I know you do," I said.

"Once you get home I'll give you a code four. Don't leave your house tonight."

"Understood. Thanks Mick. I really appreciate you answering my call," I said.

"I told you. I'll always answer your call," Mick said as he we hung up the phone.

Before leaving, I scoured my car for any and all loose change in the hopes of buying a Big Gulp before my departure. It was going to be a long night and the caffeine might come in handy. The tail eluded me when I left but I stuck with the plan. In violation of all normal op sec protocols, I parked directly in front of the store underneath the brightest light in the parking lot. Big Gulp in tow, I entered the pharmacy to check out my options for the night. Four cameras, two fire exits, and one sitting area directly in front of the pharmacy counter. A single bench, which actually had a nice cushion but lacked any surveillance coverage.

For the first hour, I walked up and down every aisle perusing every item. It was actually interesting. Next time you visit a pharmacy, I want you to really look at all of the different items they offer for sale. The second hour I spent sitting on the ground in the middle of the magazine aisle which would come to be my final resting spot. Who can beat me? Plenty of magazines. My trusty Big Gulp by my side. A view of the front door equipped with a chime. A bathroom nearby. A fire exit directly to my right and I had my own dedicated camera for my resting place.

"Hey. Are you okay?" a pharmacy clerk asked, finally getting the courage or noticing that I had been sitting there a very long time.

"Yeah. I'm fine," I said.

"Do you need anything?" he asked.

"No. I'm good. My car broke down and I'm just waiting for a buddy to pick me up. Is it okay if I hang out here a little longer?" I asked.

"Oh. That sucks. Sure," he said.

"Cool. I won't mess anything up. I promise," I said.

"Okay. I just wanted to make sure you were okay," he said.

"Thank you. I'm good," I said, but actually I wasn't. My mouth was extremely dry and my Big Gulp just wasn't getting it done. A thirst like no other. Water. *I need some water*, I thought. Standing up, I lost my balance slightly. No, I didn't fall down this time, but I was dizzy. A quick splash of water on my face hoping for a reset of my body's operations. But that didn't work. A pain in my left testicle showed up to the games being played internally, only compounding my issues. The pain wasn't severe, but very confusing, only adding to the decline of my mental state.

Beep, beep, beep. Just before midnight… 939-939-939. Mick's call sign, giving me the green light for the next phase of the counter surveillance. My dizziness tapped itself out for a headache, but it was game time and I switched to *go mode.* Focused. Forgetting about my ailments. I followed Mick's directions, traveling home and trusting the boys were out there invisible to my eyes. Pulling into my apartment I didn't see any tails but that didn't mean they weren't out there. I felt like I was being hunted, stalked by an unknown prey. I pulled into my parking spot, running over a few remaining shards of glass from the break-ins earlier in the week. I remained vigilant, looking for any ambushes that might be lurking in or around the corners or more specifically, any foot guys trying to put me in my place. They never came. I opened my door, relieved I was finally back to my shelter and anticipating a page full of 44444's.

Beep, beep, beep bounced off my walls. *There it is*, code four, I thought, but I knew it was going to take me a while to decompress to get out of *go mode*. That night I couldn't sleep much. The culprit? It's a multiple-choice test.

A) Nagging testicular pain

B) Exhaustion

C) Bone-crushing headache

D) Squirrel family having a debate in my head

E) I had all of the above, so I'm going to add it as a viable option here.

Saturday

The next morning, I woke lying on my couch still dressed in the previous day's attire. I felt like I'd wrestled an alligator all night, not certain who won the battle. My body was crampy and my headache was still there, but not as intense. The good news was my left testicular pain had subsided. It was a big day for me. My first gun purchase as a militia man was happening, along with the biggest sale of the year for my department. Not to mention, I was nervous to walk to my car knowing that someone was watching me.

The plan – Mick and G were set up on my apartment in the morning before I left to go to Big 5. Their sole mission was to determine if I had a tail on me and if I did, were they friend or foe? My instructions were to leave my apartment and drive directly to Big 5 without performing any dry-cleaning tactics myself. The team would handle that for me. Meet Tom and the militia men at the Big 5, purchase my rifle and ammunition and transport it back to my apartment where I was to secure it. Then off to work, arriving before Dan the store manager arrived. I was hoping all of that would happen by 9 AM. A lofty goal, but one that I felt confident I could achieve.

Game time. I paced back and forth in my apartment like a caged tiger, waiting for the clock to strike 7:30. My departure time. Naturally early to everything, I wanted to leave at 7:25 but the *rules guy* inside me won the battle. The clock struck 7:30 and I was off. Tom, Harold and Mike were there waiting in the parking lot at the Big 5 when I arrived, anxiously awaiting to purchase their rifles. I was surprised I didn't see Jeff and Kelly. After some small talk, the store opened up and in we went.

"Hey guys, do you mind if I go first? I'm supposed to be at work right now but I didn't want to miss this sale," I asked the group, forgetting that we were supposed to be autonomous.

"No, that's fine," Tom said and twenty minutes later I walked out of the store with an SKS rifle, 1,000 rounds of ammunition, with a few extra ammo clips and a large bag of beef jerky; I like jerky and Mick had told me to spend the money. My purchase went smooth. No hits on my cover name. I said my goodbyes to the militia boys and I was off to secure the rifle and ammunition back at my apartment. Driving extra cautious. Coming to full stops, not wanting to draw any unwanted attention to myself. Always trying to be a perfectionist, never satisfied with my performance or results in life, I began to beat myself up for leaving early. Knowing that I should have purchased my rifle last, mentally cataloguing all of the militia men's purchases to document in their files. Hopefully the surveillance team set up in the store and parking lot had picked up my slack; if not, I'd have to find out who bought what later.

9:07 – I arrived to work to an absolute shitshow. As soon as I walked in the door. "Steven. Head's up. Dan's looking for you and he's not happy, but I threw Lupe back there to cover you. She used to run that department so she got it," Mags said.

"Lupe? Where's Sal?" I asked.

"No idea. The schedule said you were opening," Mags said, throwing her hands up in the air, as I rushed to my department. Lupe had the phone in one ear as she was ringing up customers and signaling with her right hand to help a separate customer. Controlled chaos at its finest.

"Hey, Steven. Welcome. Can you grab me the sale television out from the back?" Lupe asked with her normal smile.

Shocked by the calmness of her request, I said, "Yeah. Sure."

"Great, thank you. You might want to bring out some more Kodak film while you're there," she said with another smile. Her poise and attitude surrounded by the chaos that she had been thrown into was remarkable. I returned a few minutes later with her television request, followed by a pallet of more Kodak film.

"Thank you, Steven. Much appreciated," Lupe said, continuing to navigate the onslaught of customers. "It looks like you were pretty well prepared. Nicely done. The only thing I see is that you need two end caps of Kodak film during this sale," she said.

I didn't know if that was a back-ended compliment or a dig.

"Hey. Mags put me back here with you today since no one was here to open and Sal called in sick. But don't worry. I know this department. We'll be fine," Lupe said.

"Well okay then," I said with a chuckle. Lupe and I worked over the next six hours flawlessly together, but my testicular pain came back with a vengeance followed by headaches with an occasional dizzy spell. My stubbornness or stupidity wouldn't allow me to quit or leave early, but the end of my shift couldn't come soon enough.

"We did it, Lupe! Great Job. We can turn it over to the B team now," I said jokingly.

"Yeah, right. Thank you. It was fun being back in my old department again. I enjoyed it," she said.

"Yes. It was fun. Thank you again. You were a life saver. I owe you one," I said.

"Yes you do," Lupe said with a smile. "Chocolate," she said.

"What?" I asked.

"Chocolate. I like chocolate," she repeated.

"Well, alrighty then. Chocolate it is," I said.

"Kidding. You don't owe me anything, silly. It was fun. Are you working tomorrow?" she asked.

"I am," I said.

"Me too. I'll see you then. Good luck tomorrow," she said, heading up towards the front.

Switching gears quickly, I couldn't wait to call Mick to see if everything had gone well after I'd left and to see if he and G had found out anything on my tail.

"Hey! Everything okay?" Mick asked when he answered his phone.

"Yup. I'm just clocking out. What happened? Did you guys see anything? Am I clear to leave or where are we at with everything?" I asked.

"Oh. Fuck, sorry man. I've been swamped all day and I haven't had a chance to call you yet. You were right about the tail," he said.

"Really? I knew it. Who was it?" I asked.

"It was SIS, but they weren't set up on you," Mick said.

"SIS? Holly crap," I said, knowing that if SIS is set up on you it's generally not a great outcome for their target.

"They were set up on someone in your area. It's not you. Trust me. G's old partner works SIS and filled him in. We covered it. How the hell did you ID them?" he asked.

"I don't know, man. I just got lucky I guess," I said.

"You're good. People are impressed around here, I can tell you that," Mick said.

"Confirming I'm clear to go home?" I asked, just wanting to go rest and take some drugs.

"Yeah. You're clear."

"Cool. I'm out of here then," I said, just trying to get off the phone without telling Mick that I was having some issues.

"Hey. Can you meet me tonight so I can grab that stuff from you? No, let's wait until Monday when SID is in the office so I can get it photographed," Mick continued, thinking out loud.

"Monday works better for me, Mick. Can we wait?" I asked.

"Yeah. No problem, man. Whatever works best for you."

"Thanks. I'll talk to you later," I said.

"Hey! Before you go. Great job today, man. The 6th floor is ecstatic."

"That's good to know. Later, man," I said, hanging up the phone.

Sunday

I was up and out of my apartment early and off to work, anticipating that Salvador was going to be a no show again. As long as my sales continued to crush expectations I was planning on leaving early to try to get some rest.

"Well, well, well… Good morning," Mags said as I walked in the door.

"Hey Mags. Any word from Salvador?" I asked.

"Nope. He's still MIA," she said.

"Okay, thanks," I said.

"You can't have Lupe today, Steven. I need her up front," Mags said.

"I'm good. Tell her thank you again," I said.

The day was going pretty smooth operationally but my medical woes were getting worse. The pain in my left testicle was almost unbearable followed by dizziness. I was in a pickle. Steven didn't have medical insurance and my choices were few. I opted for phone a friend. I called my sister, who was a nurse.

"Sis. How are you?" I said, thankful she'd answered her phone.

"Brother. This is a nice surprise. How are you?" she asked.

"I'm good," I answered instinctually.

"Bullshit. What's wrong?" She'd switched to MacGregor *go mode*. MacGregors have never been accused of being shy in these moments. A gene that has served as a blessing and a curse.

"Brother. You need to go to a hospital right now and get some blood work done," she said adamantly.

"I can't go right now, Sis. You don't understand, but trust me. It's not that simple. Besides. I'm not really a hospital kind of guy," I said.

"You were pre-med for three years and said you were going to be a doctor since you were six. How can you not be a hospital kind of guy? You know better and you need to get your ass to the hospital," she said.

"Sis. I can't go to the hospital right now. I'm looking for your advice to buy me some time. Is there something I can take?" I asked.

"Listen to me. There are too many things this could be. I don't know. Get your ass to the hospital. Promise me! Drew. I mean it. Get your ass to the hospital now," she continued.

"Okay. Okay. I will. I promise," I said, realizing my mistake in calling her.

"Brother. Get your ass to the hospital right now and call me back after you know something. I'm not kidding," she insisted.

"I will. I have to go, but I'll call you later," I said, just trying to get off the phone.

It didn't take long. My sister knows me very well and she knew that I had zero intention in going to the hospital. I was merely looking for her justification or an excuse not to go to the hospital. About one hour later, Claire walked up to my counter. I knew exactly why she was there.

"Hey, kid. How are you?" she said in her motherly voice.

"I'm okay. My sister?" I asked with a grin on my face.

"Yup. You should have called us. Let's go, kid. It's not negotiable."

Confused to see Claire, I asked, "Why are you here? I thought you were done with this stuff."

184

"She lost Mick's number, but she still had mine. So I got the call and here I am. I gave her Mick's number so don't worry, she has it now. Let's get you checked out, kid," Claire continued to insist. "Here's the address to the county hospital. I'm going to shadow you there. Just check in as if you were Steven. Don't worry about the bill. It's county. They have to take you and tell them you don't have any insurance or job. If it's anything serious then you're to let me know and we'll swap out your identities and use your good insurance at a normal hospital," she said.

"Isn't that a crossover? Won't it blow my cover?"

"I'm not worried about that right now. Can you drive?" Claire asked.

If you've never spent the night in a Los Angeles County hospital, let's just say it's a humbling, personal growth opportunity. Especially for your first-time hospital experience. Several hours and tests later, I remained sitting in my hospital bed that was parked in a hallway across from the maternity ward. Not enough rooms to meet the demand. Bodies stacked everywhere. All of us just a patient number, stuck on a hamster wheel waiting our turn, in hopes we could get spit out the side and off the wheel. Humanity had left the building with Elvis. I knew it was morning, but I had lost all track of time and I was wondering if my lifeline, Claire, remained nearby. Man, if my mother found out that I was in the hospital my undercover days would be over, I thought.

"Steven?" a nurse asked.

"Yes, ma'am," I replied.

"Your blood work and urinalysis showed that you are extremely dehydrated so we're going to pump some fluids through you while we wait for the doctor. Are you scared of needles?" she asked.

185

"I don't think so," I said.

"Good. I'm going to start an IV and hopefully the doctor will see you within the hour," she said.

"Sounds good," I said.

I saw the doctor about two hours later. He believed my testicular pain was a result of stress/anxiety and extreme dehydration. After a few Ivs, he told me to take it easy, ice my balls, take warm baths and if the pain persisted to follow up with my primary doctor in a week. MacGregors didn't believe in stress or anxiety... who knew that was a thing? My father had forgotten to teach me that one. I guess my body disagreed with my lifestyle and it let me know loud and clear that something had to change.

Summoned

"The question is not whether we will be extremist,
but what kind of extremist will we be."
Martin Luther King, Jr.

The Department's response to my dehydration, stress/anxiety, testicular pain diagnosis was unusually swift. Shockingly, decision making within the Department is normally very slow, painful, and frustrating. It's referred to as the *Big Blue Machine* for a reason. Not so much in this case: I was ordered to see the department psychologist and given a week on the beach. Not literally; it's cop lingo for when you get sidelined. After the orders came down I knew it wasn't worth arguing, and so my focus shifted to what lies I was going to have to tell so I could get back to work. What could I tell my work and the militias as to why I was going to be gone all week? It was easier in the beginning to disappear. Not so much the case now. I was too deep. Too entangled.

Order No. 1 – Department Psychologist

JT's crew arranged our first meeting. We met at a Department Water and Power (DWP) plant in an employee break room. It was normal for me to meet in strange locations, but I could tell that the Doc was a little green and off his game. A short, rounder fellow, about fifty years of age. Red hair, thinning, with a side part comb over. Glasses that rested on the bridge of a full nose. Pale skin, which was to be expected with the red hair.

"Hi. I'm Doctor Green. It's nice to meet you," he said, reaching out to shake my hand.

"Nice to meet you," I said.

"This is a first for me," he said, looking around at the DWP break room with JT's guys standing outside guarding the door like they were secret service agents.

I just laughed. "Unfortunately, it's not for me. You'll get used to it," I said, trying to lighten the mood.

"Really? What do you mean by that?" he asked.

"Not that I've seen a shrink before. I didn't mean that, Doc. I meant; with my lifestyle it seems like I always end up in strange places. That's all. It's a new normal for me," I said.

"Well, I'm told that I am limited in what I can ask you and what you can talk about. What shall I call you?" he asked.

"Mac works for me. I always liked that name," I said.

"Mac it is. So, what brings you here today?" he asked.

Perplexed by his question, I said, "I was ordered to be here. May I ask you what marching orders they gave you?"

"Marching orders? What do you mean by that?" he asked.

"Oh, sorry, Doc. I was just curious about what they'd told you about me and why we're meeting?" I said, seemingly playing a cat and mouse game. But, I really was curious about how all this had unfolded.

The Doc and I spoke for an hour. The conversation did not flow and it was really awkward to be honest. The Doc's mission was two-fold based on his line of questioning:

1. To provide me with stress relief techniques.
2. To determine if I was suicidal.

The problem was he didn't have the clearance to know what I was doing. He would run through scenarios about what caused me stress during the course of my duties, and I couldn't tell him. It was a big joke and I honestly felt bad for him because he really was trying to do his job. After thirty minutes of trying, we gave up and talked about his family until we reached the required hour time limit.

189

"It was fascinating to talk to you, Mac. Maybe someday I'll find out some answers to the questions I really want to ask you. Here's my card. Call me anytime," he said.

Looking down at his card, I committed his phone number to memory. "Thanks, Doc, but I can't take your card. But I have your number and if I need anything I'll certainly give you a call," I said.

"Wait. Why can't you take my card?" he asked.

"It's considered a crossover, Doc. But don't worry, I know your number," I said.

The Doc took back his card not knowing how to react. I could tell that he wanted me to prove that I had memorized his phone number that quickly. I was certain he was going to ask me; but he didn't.

Order No. 2 – Week on the Beach

Literally this time! I wanted to go home, but I was worried if something happened that I would put Gary and my family at risk. The militias were really on edge during this time and it was very unusual for me to be gone for an entire week with such short notice. I don't really remember what lie or cover story I came up with, but I do remember it sucked.

The Department put me up in a hotel near the beach per my request. Water has always had a calming effect on me, which remains the case today. I didn't tell any of my family or friends that I was sidelined for the week. I just wanted to hit the reset button. But there was one person I wanted to see: Liz.

For the first two days I slept, but I didn't have much of an appetite. A few long walks on the beach. The same school of dolphins swam by in the mornings, but I never made it into the water. It was freezing. The days seemed long to me. My mind, racing in between two lives. A living purgatory. Not knowing which life was God's work or path for me. Liz. Lonely, I wanted and needed Liz. My phone calls, unscheduled, went unanswered. I was going stir crazy and couldn't help but think about the militias.

On day four, Liz called me back.

"Babe? What number is this? Are you here?" she asked. There was something I picked up in the inflection of her voice. I knew instantly but I did not want to believe it.

"Hi, babe. Yes, I'm here but just for a week. I was hoping to see you?" I said.

"Okay! Umm... Yes. Where are you at?" Liz asked excitedly.

"I'm in Manhattan Beach, but I have to stay here. I can't go anywhere," I said.

"Umm. Okay. Tomorrow. I can come tomorrow. What time?" she asked.

"Liz. It's okay... It's okay. Do I know him?" I asked.

She didn't answer.

"It's not your fault. You didn't ask for this. I don't blame you, but you could have told me," I said and I heard her holding back tears.

"I was going to tell you but I wanted to tell you in person and not over the phone. And it's not like I can just call you. Damn, I don't even know where you're at," she said through a steady stream of tears.

"I know. You're right," I said, still in shock. I wasn't mad. I wasn't even sad. At that moment, crazy as it seemed, my focus was on trying to figure out how I'd known that something was wrong after she'd spoken only a few words. It freaked me out.

"It's your fault. We were supposed to go and get married and then you chose that assignment over me! Who told you? How did you know? You had me followed, huh?" she asked angrily as the Latina awoke.

"No, babe. I didn't have you followed," I said, laughing slightly.

"I know you did. That's bullshit, Mac," she said, tears turning to anger. "He wants to marry me and start a family, unlike you, Mac."

"That's not fair, Liz. But I'm glad you're happy," I said, feeling bad that I'd hurt her. Knowing it was my choice.

"I am happy, Mac. He treats me well but this should be us. He loves me. He chooses me. You didn't," she continued.

"Well, I'm sad it ended this way, babe. But I honestly don't blame you. It was a big ask. You deserve to be happy," I said.

Silence. Reflection and more silence. Neither one of us believing it was over but knowing that it was. Our whirlwind relationship was over. It wasn't the way I'd had it playing out in my mind but if it had to be done, I guessed this was the week to do it. Life. It's about choices we make. But do we really understand that the choices we make during those moments can change the trajectory of our lives?

Order No. 3 – Medical Clearance

Back to the doctor. This time as Mac, equipped with the best medical insurance offered: the Police Department's Blue Cross PPO. Treated as a human in clean facilities where patient care was actually practiced. More tests, blood work, etc. You all know the routine.

Militia Drama

I was at the end of the pier looking at the fisherman's catch of the day. Blood on the deck and fish in the bucket. Seemed like a good day. *Beep, beep, beep*... 939-333. It was Mick paging me code three, but I didn't see a payphone anywhere in sight. Luckily I had my running shoes on and off I went searching for a payphone. I found one bank of payphones but quickly realized that I didn't have any money on me. Hotel room it was...

"Hey, Mick. What's up?" I asked, out of breath.

"What took you so long? What's wrong with you?" Mick asked.

"I ran my happy ass here because there are no gosh darn payphones down here where you rich people live. Only in the ghetto. I had to run back to my hotel to call you," I said, still out of breath.

"Are you finished or do you need a little more time?" Mick asked.

"With me venting or with my time on the beach?" I asked.

"Something is going on with the groups and we need you but I'm not supposed to be talking to you. Do you hear me," Mick said.

"I hear you. What's going on with the groups?" I asked.

"Not sure. That's why we need you. Did you get your medical clearance?" he asked.

"I don't know. I thought you would know that but I'm good. Get me out of here. Let's go," I said.

"I can't get you out of there. We're not supposed to be talking, you jackass. You have to get yourself out and don't tell them I called you or I'll get in trouble again," Mick said.

"How am I going to do that?" I asked.

"I don't know. You're the undercover guy, not me," he said.

My only shot was to see if Jay could get me off the beach. I didn't think Samantha had the juice. JT would say no, just to say no. Jack… Nope. I called Jay and explained my situation. Jay said he would make it happen and come pick me up in a couple of hours. Jay delivered and I was back as a militia man by nightfall. I was only gone five days but it seemed like a lifetime.

Mick was right. Something was going on with the militias. There was a page on my militia pager from Tom: *55-123* (*call to arms*). *Wow, that can't be good*, I thought. Why was there a militia armed call-up?

"Hey, Tom. What's going on?" I asked, purposefully elusive.

"Did you get my page?" he asked.

"I did. That's why I'm calling," I said.

"Good. But I don't want to talk on the phone. Can you meet me?"

"Sure. Let's meet at the same place we met last time," I said.

"Okay. I'll see you there in thirty minutes," Tom said.

I met Tom at the Barnes and Noble parking lot. He said, "The San Diego militia commander called for an emergency meeting of the Southern California militias. His goal is to get organized on all levels. There's a commanders' meeting tonight to discuss the event in two weeks' time. Denali Park, us, Orange County, Cypress, Anaheim, La Verne and San Fernando Valley militias will all be represented tonight. I need you. Can you make it?"

"Yeah, I can make it. Do you want me to pick you up?" I asked.

"No. I'll meet you there," Tom said in a rattled voice.

"Wait. Did you say the event's in two weeks?" I asked.

"Yes. In two weeks," Tom said.

"What the hell, Tom? Why would you page us with a *call to arms* when the meeting is in two weeks?"

"Yeah, I know. I thought of that after. Well, they want us armed but it's not really a *call to arms*. We should add another pager code next meeting," he said.

"Tom, did the other guys go to the rally points? You know that's what we're supposed to do if you send out that page right?" I asked.

"Fuck, you're right! I didn't think of that. Let me send out another page."

"I think that would be a good idea," I said, shaking my head. "I have to go but I'll see you tonight," I said.

I stopped at my usual stomping grounds to call Mick to let him know what was going on from my end. Not knowing if that would match up with the chatter he'd been referring to.

"Hi, this is Jules!" she answered.

"Hey Jules, it's Steven," I said.

"Oh shit! Hold on, let me get Mick," she said.

"Jules, Jules… It's okay. I'm good…"

"No, you don't understand, I got yelled at last time that I talk too much. So just tell me to shut up next time okay," she said, making me laugh.

Jules. We have yet to meet and I knew nothing about her, except that I liked her. She sounded fun and a good match for Mick.

"Hey! What do you got?" Mick asked.

"There's a militia call-up in two weeks down in San Diego. They want me to go. Do you guys want me to go?" I asked.

"Fuck yeah we want you to go! That's awesome. FBI is going to shit," Mick said.

"Why? What happened with the FBI?" I asked.

"They've been trying to figure this out for days. I said fuck it and called you and you have the answer that night. They're going to shit. Are you sure?" Mick asked.

"I'm sure. There's a commanders' meeting tonight to discuss the details. Allegedly, there are going to be militias from all over Southern California attending. They want to organize," I said.

"Wow! That's huge. And you can attend that?" Mick asked.

"Yup. Of course I can. I'm a militia man," I said, making fun of my situation.

"Hey. I'm outta here. I call you later and tell you where the meeting is."

"Hey. Thanks again, man. You have no idea how much this helps," Mick said as we hung up the phone.

Mindset

The five days on the beach provided me some clarity in two worlds that were unclear. I realized that everything I was doing was part time. My two lives were broken into the pieces of two puzzles. Neither of which seemed to be solvable. The pieces, life events, couldn't be transferred from one puzzle to the next. Was I living part time as Mac in Steven's body or was I living as Mac part time in Steven's body? It was confusing in every aspect. Was I a part time cop, disguised as a militia man? Or was it the other way around? I lived, worked and befriended many people that valued my friendship as did I; including criminals that I had a new understanding of, all under a cloak of lies that would someday come crashing down. Naturally a planner, I did not see a good ending. There was no viable exit strategy. Longing for my family and friends, but knowing that I was well past the undercover depths of return to have any meaningful relationship with them right now. Realizing that any and all friendships that Steven developed were terminal and based on layer after layer of lies. I felt trapped and forced to choose a life. A name. A home. A job. Friends. Not because anyone told me to. But because I could no longer live a bifurcated life. I saw it as my only logical path to sanity, without having a mental breakdown or a heart attack. I chose to honor *my word* and fulfill my commitment, however long that took.

Lunchtime

Back to work for a couple of days now and it was actually pleasantly boring. My department was slow and drama free. Lupe called me up shortly after I arrived to work.

"Hey Steven. You're back. I heard you had a family emergency. Is everything okay?"

"Yeah. I'm good. Thank you for asking. How are you?" I asked.

"I'm great. I'm coming to see you." She hung up the phone quickly. My department had to be staffed at all times with someone babysitting the cash register. Similar to house arrest but in a department store.

"Hi. I wanted to come give you a hug. Sorry, I'm a hugger. I hope everything is okay with your family," she said, genuinely concerned about my lie.

"Thank you, Lupe. Everything is okay. How have you been?" I asked, trying to switch topics.

"May I ask what happened?" she said.

"Another time. I'd rather not talk about it if that's okay," I said, and she of course agreed. Not the pushy confrontational type.

"Okay. No problem. Hey, I have to go back up front but I just wanted to make sure you're okay," she said, running back to the front.

I called an audible... and dialed the front of the store.

"Mags... what can I do for you?" Her standard line.

"Mags. Did Lupe make it back up there yet?" I asked.

"Well. I see her running this way. This girl cracks me up. Hold on. Lupe, it's for you," Mags said.

"This is Lupe," she said, out of breath from her apparent jog.

"Hey! It's me. You took off too fast. Lunch today?" I asked.

"Ahh that's sweet. I brought my lunch, dear. But we can sit together if you like. What time do you want to go?" she asked.

"I can go any time after 11, assuming my help comes in," I said.

"Hey Mags, I'm going to take my lunch at 12. Does that work for you?" Lupe asked.

"Of course, dear," I heard in the background.

"12, see you up front. Bye," Lupe said, hanging up the phone.

A few hours later the department operator paged me over the intercom. "Steven. Call the operator please. Steven, call the operator." It was a strange page.

"This is Steven," I said, after calling the operator.

"Steven. It's Alyson. I have Salvador on the line for you. He said it's important," she said.

"Sal is on the line? Oh wow. Okay, put him through to my department line please, not this phone," I said. My phone started to ring as I shuffled back over to my department phone.

"Sal? You okay man?" I asked.

"No. I'm sorry, man. Do I still have a job?" he asked.

"I don't know. What happened and why haven't you called me? I was worried and no one could get ahold of you," I said.

"Yeah. I know. I left you hangin'. I know. I'm sorry man. I really am!" I believed his tone.

"What happened?" I asked again.

"I'm embarrassed to tell you," he said.

"Just tell me!" I replied.

"I was crossing the border with my cousin in the trunk and I got caught," he said.

"You were what?" I said, not believing what I was hearing.

"I tried to sneak my cousin across the border and I got caught. I don't know how or why. I've done it a few times before and never had an issue. Fucking dogs, man. Damn dog got me. I hate dogs."

"Sal. What were you thinking?" I asked him.

"Steven. I need that job, man. Do I still have one?" he asked.

"Let me see what I can do and I'll get back to you," I said.

"When will you get back to me?" he asked.

"Give me until tomorrow and I'll call you and let you know where we're at. Okay?" I said, before hanging up the phone and looking at the clock. Both hands, straight up and down. Lunch time.

Lupe was already sitting at the back table where most employees sit.

"Hey you. Did you order your lunch already?" Lupe asked.

"I did. Thank you. It should be ready shortly," I said.

"What did you get?" she asked.

"Just a grilled cheese sandwich and chips," I said.

"Really? I didn't expect that. I see you more as a meat burger type," Lupe said.

I started to laugh. "Well, I am that guy too. Just not today, I guess," I replied.

Time flew by and our allotted time was over for lunch but since we were both department heads we bent the rules, slightly, extending our lunches.

"Hey. I want your help. Well, your opinion on something, if you're willing?" I asked her.

"Sure. So is that why you asked me to lunch? You need my help?" she said, looking at me in anticipation of my response.

"No. Not at all," I said.

"So, you don't need my help?" she asked.

"Well, yes. I mean no. Let me start over. I asked you to lunch because I wanted to go to lunch with you. No, I don't need your help with anything, but I would like your opinion on an employee issue I have, because I value your opinion. Does that make sense?" I asked.

"Yes. I understood. I was just having a little fun. What do you need my opinion on?" she asked, turning all of her attention towards me.

"It's Sal. You remember what happened with him during electronics week? He called me today to apologize. He had a great excuse why he didn't show and why he couldn't call that I don't want to go into because it's personal, but he wants to know if he still has a job. What do you think?" I asked.

"I love Sal! I trained Salvador and that was very unlike him, so I'm certain he had a great reason. It's his family, huh?" Lupe asked.

"Why do you ask that?" I said.

"This kid does everything for his family. Last time I spoke with him he was working three jobs and sending money back to Mexico to try and get his family over here to the States. He's still just a kid but is the man of the house. I don't know how he does it."

"That answered my question. Thank you. See, I knew you could help me," I said.

"That helped you?" she asked.

"Yes it did. We better get out of here. You're setting a bad example," I said.

"Oh, I'm setting a bad example and you're not?" Lupe said with a laugh.

"Exactly. I'm glad we see eye to eye again," I said, jokingly.

"You're impossible! Hey I think they already processed Sal's paperwork as job abandonment," Lupe said.

"Really? How do I fix that?" I asked.

"You have to go through the Dan," she said.

"Oh great," I said, laughing.

"Good luck with that." Lupe said as we got up to leave.

"Same time tomorrow?" I asked.

"Sure. I would love to. See you then," Lupe said, trotting off back towards her front of store duties as I saw Dan standing in the lunch line. No better time than the present, I thought.

"Steven. How are you? Great job again on the electronics sale. You smashed your numbers," Dan said, as I saw my opportunity.

"Hey Dan. I had a question. There must have been some type of mix up on Salvador. I forgot who told me but they said that his paperwork was being processed for job abandonment?" I asked.

"Yeah. That's what Sandy told me," Dan said as he scanned the menu.

"I don't know where the mix up is. But he called me and asked for time off for personal reasons and I approved it," I said as Dan turned towards me.

"Sal called you for time PT and you approved it? Did he or you fill out a PT request and get it signed by Sandy?" Dan asked.

"No. I didn't. Sorry. I honestly didn't know he had to put in a formal request. I just took him off my schedule," I said.

"No. That's not how it works, Steven. You have to go through Sandy for that stuff. Go tell her what happened and don't do that again," he said, refocusing on his stomach.

"Okay. Will do, sir. Sorry about that, but I got it now," I said, heading to the back of the store to make sure Sal had a job. Luckily, because Sal had been a great employee it wasn't an issue and I was able to save his job, adding another lie to my soul. But that lie actually felt good. I called Sal up immediately.

"Salvador! When can you work?" I asked.

"Really? I have a job?" he asked, elated.

"You do. You've earned another shot. When can you work?" I asked.

"I can work right now, sir. Anytime. I'm open. I need the money," he said.

"See you when you get here, buddy," I said.

"Really? Okay. I'll be right there, sir," he said.

I gave Salvador my hours that day and took the rest of the night off. It was a great day for me.

Militia Call-Up

The militia call-up was the first of its kind, at least in California, and I had a ticket to the show. The call-up was put out to all of the Southern California active militias by the San Diego militia commander who had grown frustrated over the lack of structure, organization, and mission of the militias. I had no idea what to expect, how many militias were invited and more importantly how many were going to answer the call. A litmus test of the movement was the way that I saw it.

Al, Mick and I had a meeting the day prior to discuss my mission, but more importantly I received a free meal. Denny's again. The Yankee pot roast and a Dr. Pepper this time.

"Are you ready for this, kid?" Al asked me, hiding behind the sports section of the *LA Times*.

"Sure," I said. But he didn't understand that I didn't need to get *ready* anymore. It was my life. "Are you guys ready?" I asked, looking at Mick.

"Almost," he said. "We're going to have a contingency in the area but I don't want to go into all of the details with you. You just play militia boy and do your thing."

Al, not missing a beat, turned to page 2.

"I will. Can you play detective for once and do something?" I said jokingly to Mick, causing Al to lower his newspaper and look at me over his glasses. We started to laugh.

"Hey. I'm outta here. See you when I see you, boys. Thanks for the lunch," I said, getting up.

The Rainier Park and Denali Park militias had a 1600 rally time at the Target parking lot near the call-up location in Borrego Springs. Eleven vehicles caravanning together to our final destination, a camping ground near the Salton Sea. *Why would we caravan?* I thought. *Can we make this any easier for ATD?* There was an excitement in the air. The movement wasn't any different than a small business, sports team, or the third largest metropolitan police department in the nation. They craved leadership, direction, organization, and purpose. Would this call-up appease the movement's growing appetite for those fruits we all crave and desire?

Friday 1800 – Briefing

Rick, dressed in full desert camo attire, boots to boonie hat, addressed the group of sixty-three militia men. Not a single woman in attendance. Security checks were absent and left to each unit's commander. Men gathered in clusters separated by units. Smorgasbord of militia men. Full camo with rank insignias and arm patches proudly displaying their unit's name. Others looked like cops or firemen hanging out around a firepit telling lies and stories about the good ol' days when they were something. Regardless, they'd come! The movement was real.

204

A schedule was passed out to each unit laying out the weekend's events and security detail sign-up slots required by each unit. Inclusive in the schedule hand-out were the *do's and don'ts* and the *rules of engagement* if a government agent or seize were to be encountered. The first night objectives were simple: get everyone settled and fill up the security detail slots. The real business was scheduled to start in the morning. The San Diego unit covered the first night's security shift, 1800–0200. Four armed militia men covering the winds. Eight-hour shifts, standing your post around the perimeter of the campsite looking for government agents, news media, or undesirables. The northern end of the campsite was reserved and cordoned off with yellow police tape from the general public, but camping near the Salton Sea didn't make most vacationers' top camping destination list anyway.

Jason addressed both the Denali Park and Rainier Park militia units at our campsites after Rick had finished the general briefing. "Men. Thanks for making the trip. I am cautiously optimistic about this weekend's call-up. It's great to see so many of our fellow countrymen here and I know the commanders did not extend an invite to all of their members. Rest assured, there are many more of us than this. For tonight, I'm looking for volunteers to cover our security detail obligation. We have the second shift, 0200–1000 hours. Tom, can I get two from your unit and I'll take two from mine."

"Sure," Tom said and I gave him the nod that I'd be one of the two.

"Great. Make sure you're in uniform. We want to be clearly identifiable if we're going to be armed. Rifles with secondary weapons. Rules of engagement are do not fire unless fired upon. If you come across any unfriendlies, put it out over the radio and immediately ask for back-up.

Media enquiries? We're gun enthusiasts. That's it. If you need relief call either Tom or I. Do not leave your post. Any questions?" Jason asked.

"No, sir," the group answered.

"Alright. Let's do it," Jason said.

"I have Steven, Jeff, Ralph and Johnny for the second shift. Is that correct?" Tom asked and we all nodded.

"Thank you. Don't be late to your post," Tom said.

Restless sleep. Dozing in and out of consciousness not wanting to miss my security detail assignment. Checking my equipment just as I used to do prior to my patrol shifts. SKS rifle slung across my body locked and loaded, ready for any government agent provocateurs. I did not own a secondary weapon, pistol, but I was the minority. The four of us headed out to our posts in the middle of the night fifteen minutes early, making sure we arrived on time. I relieved Joe from the San Diego militia. A shorter man, but one of the few fit militia men that I saw. Older than me, but I would still put him in the younger bucket, around thirty-five. Full beard, attentive, and took his post more seriously than most cops standing on a wanted suspect perimeter. My guess would be he was former military. Dressed in night ops camo, blacked out with a full load-out of gear. Tactical vest with six magazine pouches across his chest. Glock thigh rig was his choice for a secondary weapon system. Primary, a Car-15-style rifle seated with a thirty-round magazine attached to a three-point sling.

"I'm Joe. Welcome to my security post. Thanks for the relief," he said.

"Steven. Nice to meet you," I said as we shook hands.

206

"Here's your radio. Stay on base, channel 14. Base camp will check in with all posts at the top of every hour. Just acknowledge. Also, if you have any requests or need anything you can go through base. Any questions?"

"No. I think I'm good. Go get some shut eye,'' I said.

"See you in the morning," Joe said with a firm pat on my back.

Standing my post was surreal. Gripping my SKS rifle fully loaded with 7.62x39 mm. A nasty round. Walking back and forth in the middle of the night fulfilling my duties to protect the militia against guys like me. Hoping Al, Mike, G or whoever else was out there didn't get shot at by an overzealous militia man looking to earn his stripes. It was thought-provoking. Disturbing. Intense at times, trying to decipher if the night sounds were real.

"Base to post one," I heard over the radio.

"Go for post one," Jeff answered.

"All good?" the man asked.

"All good," Jeff responded.

"Base to post two," I heard next.

"All good at post two sir," I replied.

"Thank you, sir," the voice responded as he continued roll call to the remaining two posts. Like clock-work. The process was repeated every hour on the hour.

The shift was long, ending at 1000 hours, but the sunrise was amazing. My feet hurt, I was hungry, and tired. I need to get some more comfortable boots, I thought. Too bad I couldn't wear my police boots. They were so comfortable. Back to my tent to take a quick nap. My next assignment wasn't scheduled until after lunch, which was not provided. The festivities were already in full force.

The commanders and second-in-commands met in one section of the camp and discussed a variety of ideas, suggestions, and thoughts on how to organize, focus, recruit and train the Southern California militias. Other militia members could roam freely and choose from different training sessions offered throughout the day. After dinner, the group would be together as one, debriefing the day's activities/progress and soapboxing.

Commander Topics

A.R.M (American Registry of Militia)

An idea by a tri-state militia sympathizer named Roger. Organization by creating a national militia registry. Call it a militia phone tree. ARM would house and classify members by rank, jurisdiction, equipment, and special talents. Commanders were the pipeline to ARM, submitting applications on members' behalves after passing a background for security purposes. Good idea if you were in the private sector or a government agency. However, from a movement perspective that subscribed to the terrorist philosophy of cell protection at least in theory, the idea was on the other side of the spectrum. Roger was instantly viewed as a government plant even though there was little to no proof he actually was. I was still standing my post when Roger so boldly proposed his militia registry, but the radio chatter was interesting.

"Base to Post 1. Base to Post 1. We have a potential security breach. Meet at the entrance for assistance," a man's voice spouted over the radio, just before the end of my shift. Jeff acknowledged and headed to investigate. When Jeff arrived he saw Roger being escorted off the property by two militiamen he didn't know. Base camp wanted a show of force; that's why they'd summoned Jeff.

"Roger. You are not in an active militia therefore your presence here is not welcome. You will be allowed to leave today, but if you return you will be classified as an enemy combatant and handled appropriately," Rick said to the Roger. Jeff told me later that the conversation was heated, slightly confrontational, but no one had pulled their weapons or got stabbed. A sarcastic shot. Maybe even warranted and definitely funny for Jeff's cardboard personality. Roger was escorted off the camp grounds without any real resistance and told to never come back.

Tom finished his commander's session and woke me up for lunch, bringing me a plate of food. Simple: a sandwich, apple and a bottle of water. I felt good. The hour-and-a-half nap served me well.

"Hey. Is your rifle still hot?" Tom asked me, looking at my SKS lying next to me where Liz once was.

"Yeah. It is," I said.

"Let's unload. And I want you to come to this next commander's meeting. It's on standardizing training. Are you up for it?" he asked.

"Yeah. When is it?" I asked.

"Thirty minutes. Just eat or do what you need to do and then head over there," Tom said.

"Okay. I'll meet you over there," I said.

Lunch was as good as a soggy sandwich could be, but the apple was crisp, just the way I like them. The commander's meet location was on the other side of the camp grounds. About a quarter mile walk. My dogs were still barking from standing a post all night, but they loosened up quickly once I was underway, walking along the paved internal road of the campsite towards the public restroom. Then I saw a man riding a black beach cruiser along the road in my direction. The bicycle swerving slightly from left to right, back left, then right, struggling to keep a smooth straight line. I can't remember exactly what he was wearing but I distinctly remember a baseball cap, unusually large, thick glasses and a backpack. It was Mick! What the hell was he doing? What were those glasses? When was the last time this man had ridden a bike? If he kept going down that road he was going to get jacked by a few militiamen. All these questions ran through my brain as he pedaled nearer. We locked eyes through his thick Poindexter glasses. Both of us remained in character, but I don't know how I didn't burst into laughter. The whole package was something. Chest puffed. Feathers on full display. So proud.

M.O.S.T (Militia Officer Standard Training)

Jax and Rick were presenting the next commander session. I recognized him immediately. It was the Asian dude from the Granada Forum who I'd lost track of during TJ's talk. Jax introduced himself as a commander of one of the cells within Orange County but did not give any further details.

"Welcome, guys. As you all know we need to train and there are a ton of ideas on what and how we need to train. Which Jax and I both agree on. However, what we're proposing is standardizing training for all Southern California militias. If we have standardized training broken down into basic, intermediate and advanced, everyone here will know what each cell's capabilities are and we could also integrate cells down the road if it comes to that and everyone will be on the same page," Rick said to the group and everyone seemed to like what they were hearing.

210

"Listen. We don't need to reinvent the wheel here. Police have what is called P.O.S.T. – Police Officer Standardized Training. I have mirrored that concept and developed M.O.S.T. – Militia Officer Standard Training," Jax said. His voice didn't match his appearance. He had pronounced Asian physical features, but he spoke without any hint of an accent. Moved confidently and dressed modestly, with no weapon that I could see. Comfortable speaking in front of a group, holding a pen in his hand as his designated pacifier. No shakes or dry mouth evident. He didn't have cop eyes, but his mannerisms were similar.

The group welcomed his idea and we broke off into groups to discuss what M.O.S.T levels one, two and three would look like. After two hours of bickering back and forth on what should make the list, we accomplished the goal and level one of M.O.S.T. was born. Commanders agreed to finalize their suggestions for level two training and turn it in to Rick or Jax by the time they left. Level three training was sidelined until a later date. Here are some of the highlights of the two-page document:

M.O.S.T. – Level One
- o Basic Equipment List established
- o Security Protocols
- o Unit Size
- o Basic Emergency Preparedness for individuals and for each unit
- o Weapons
  - o Rifle with 1,000 rounds
  - o Pistol with 1,000 rounds
- o Quarterly Qualification
  - o Rifle – 100 yards

o   Pistol – 25 yards

After we broke from the meeting, I ventured over to gauge the other training classes in session. Here are a few that I remember: HAM Radio operation, battlefield first aid, load-outs, marksmanship, and emergency preparedness. Walking through the many different camps and training sessions, I knew there were too many militia men running around in their BDU PJs for me to keep track of. The chances of me committing the numerous names, license plates, descriptions, and all the questions my handlers were going to have for me were slim. Besides, I'm not good with names. I saw my invitation to such a momentous event as a success in itself and I didn't worry about the masses. I remained focus on identifying anyone or any other group that was connected to the city.

Later that evening, I left for a walk to see if I could see Mick or any of the ATD crew off spying in the darkness. When I returned, Gary was sitting by our campfire talking with Tom, Jason, Joel and Paul. They motioned for me to join the discussion. Gary claimed to be the commander of the San Fernando militia cell which had two LAPD officers and one Sheriff as members. San Fernando, located in the Valley, wasn't too far from where I lived, but I had never heard of Gary or his group before and I was surprised about his law enforcement claim.

"Gary. The KLC militia has been expanding and we currently have two cells in the Los Angeles area. Our goal is to have ten cells operating in and around Los Angeles within a year. What are your thoughts about joining our group?" Paul asked.

"I kinda like my own thing. My group is very private and law enforcement heavy," he said.

"We have law enforcement within our ranks. We see that as a positive, not a negative," Paul said as Jax joined the discussion.

"Did you say that you're law enforcement, Gary?" Jax asked.

"No. I have law enforcement in my group," Gary said.

"So fucking what? I'm law enforcement. We also have former military in our group. That's a good thing. What's your point?" Jax said.

"Oh, you are?" Gary said, seemingly surprised by Jax's response.

"I am. What's the big fucking deal?" Jax said, frustrated.

Gary didn't have a response to that.

"Listen. There are two types of groups: the soap boxers and the doers. If you want to keep talking about black helicopters, implanted chips, then so be it. But me and my group are tired of that shit and are getting prepared. We're training hard. Quit talking about fucking black helicopters and learn how to shoot them down! For fucksake!" Jax said.

"I agree with Jax," Joel said.

"Me and my group will open our training up to local militias. We train out in 29 Palms and in the San Dimas area. If you guys want to come just let me know," Jax said.

Tom and I made eye contact and I gave him the metro nod.

"Hey Jax. Our group would like to go to your next training," Tom said, followed by Jason adding, "Yeah, so would ours. We'd like to check it out."

"Great! Let's fucking do this. I think you'll be impressed by our training. We have a 2.5-mile desert course, where we patrol with multiple targets along the way. Also, we have a rifle qualification course set up out to 300 yards. It's pretty good," Jax said.

"When do you think you'll have your training?" Tom asked.

"I'll give you our schedule. It has all of our training sessions and meetings on it. You and your group are more than welcome to attend our meetings. We have an open meeting followed by a members only meeting. You guys can attend the open meeting anytime you want," Jax said.

"Is it just your group that's doing this?" Paul asked.

"It is now I guess. We were part of the Orange County militia but now we're doing our own thing," Jax said.

"What happened?" Joel asked.

"I'm just tired of their bullshit," Jax said.

"What bullshit?"

"They do nothing. They don't want to train. They just want to get together once a month and bitch. We're not about that. So we left," Jax said.

"Oh wow! That sucks," Jason said.

"It's all good. It's actually better. So, the La Verne and Cypress groups broke away and we're doing our own thing. Well. We're training together, but are separate. Billy runs the Cypress group. He's squared away, but couldn't make it this weekend. You'll meet him. Good guy," Jax said.

The conversation continued late into the night. Jax and I hit it off, bantering back and forth. I liked him and he liked what he saw in our group. New. Moldable. He seemed normal for a militia man and was easy to talk to. Maybe it was our inner intangible law enforcement traits that connected us. Maybe it was he was just the most normal person I had met that didn't want to talk about some batshit crazy conspiracy theory that seemed so far out of reach for my intellect and reality. I'm not sure, but I pegged his personality quickly. Patience would be rewarded with

214

information. Prodding, inquisitiveness, prying would put you in the penalty box. A blanket statement, but most cops don't trust anyone, especially someone that asked personal questions. Including their own mothers. It wasn't the way in with him but I felt his egocentric personality struggling. His ego was in a pickle. Proud of his group's accomplishments, not only desiring, but needing to brag to the world about them. Unable, knowing it would draw attention to his group with eventual exposure. It was just a matter of time. I felt Jax couldn't help himself. Patience was the key. I knew that information wouldn't flow freely but it would come piece by piece, jigsaw style. Puzzles were always my grandfather's deal not mine. But I knew G-man was the master of all puzzles.

Driving back home from the Salton Sea, Restless Heart's 'Fast Movin Train' began to play, bringing me back to Mac's life. Gary and I loved that song, I have no idea why. Listening to it today, it's not a great song. No idea. Vulnerable. Feeling sorry for myself. Coming off such a high emotion from the militia call-up to an instant low. The emotional rollercoaster was new to me and something I'd never had to deal with before. I didn't understand it. I couldn't control it. So I did what all young men do when they don't know anything else and feel threatened by emotions. Acted out, slapping myself across the face, similar to a fighter before entering the ring.

Smack! It hurt more than I was expecting.

Smack! I think that did it, I thought.

The Shrink probably would not agree with my choice, but it seemed to work until I saw a red light in my rear-view mirror, followed by a siren. I panicked. Feeling like a criminal, my heart rate increased, suddenly realizing that I actually might be a criminal and not transporting my rifle

215

and ammunition according to the letter of the law. I pulled off to the side of the road, rolling down my driver and passenger side windows, placing both of my hands on top of the steering wheel in plain sight. I saw the highway patrolman approaching my vehicle on the passenger side. He was walking casual, talking on the radio, most likely running my plate for warrants. He didn't have his hand on his gun like I was taught to do when making a traffic stop in south Los Angeles.

"Hello there. Can you turn your vehicle off for me please?" the officer said, making me feel stupid that I'd forgotten the most important step.

"Oh. Sure. Sorry about that, Officer," I said respectfully.

"May I see your driver's license, registration and insurance please?" the officer asked.

"Yes. It's in my glove box. Is it okay if I get it?" I asked.

"Sure. Have you ever been arrested before?" the officer asked me.

"No sir. I haven't," I said.

"You seem well versed in the protocol," he said.

"I live in a bad area in the Los Angeles suburbs, sir. LAPD doesn't play around," I said.

"Ahh. Got it. Where are you headed?" he asked.

"I'm just headed home, sir," I said.

"And the address on your license is home?" he asked.

"Yes, sir. It is," I said, not offering up too much information.

"Where are you coming from?" he asked.

"I went camping with some buddies and now I'm heading home," I said.

"Okay. The reason why I stopped you is that I saw you slapping yourself. What's that about? Are you okay?" he said.

"Oh that. Yes, sir. I didn't think I was speeding," I said.

"No. You weren't. But I was right next to you when you started slapping yourself," he said.

"Yes. I started to doze off a bit so I wanted to wake myself up," I said.

The officer chuckled. "Okay. Hang tight for me. I'll be right back," he said, walking back to his vehicle. I knew the militia boys would be passing by me soon since I was one of the first to leave the call-up and this was the only highway back to Los Angeles. I was worried for this officer. The militia boys were fired up and a little trigger hungry. If they saw me pulled over by an officer would they think it was the *New World Order*? *Think, Mac. What will they do? Will they pull over and try to rescue me? Will they go to guns and ambush this officer?*

"Steven. Here is your license, registration and insurance card back. You are free to go, but do me a favor and stop at the next stop. Maybe get a bite to eat, throw some water on your face to wake up. Don't hit yourself anymore, please," he said, chuckling.

"Yes, sir. I will and thank you," I said.

"Drive safe," he said, walking away. I couldn't believe I just got pulled over by an officer for hitting myself in the face. The officer, diligent in his duties, had pulled me over without the probable cause most scream about today. Solely with his oath in mind, to *protect and serve*, realizing that *The Thin Blue Line* is real. Fulfilling his oath and duty could have cost him his life for no reason, and he didn't even know it.

217

Debrief

Later that night Mick and I met at a Denny's in between our two homes to debrief the weekend's escapades. I was tired but excited to debrief. This was the first event that I knew ATD had a contingency of investigators monitoring and gathering intelligence on, independent of me, and I wanted to know how it had gone. I was surprised. I didn't see Al, but Mick was sitting in our usual spot. We gave the all-clear sign and I took my seat. An ice-cold Coke was waiting for me.

"You're a good date, you know that? You ordered my soda for me. Thank you," I said to Mick as we shook hands.

"I am a good date, but it's not full service so don't get any ideas," Mick said with a tired laugh.

"Not tonight. But you might have to consider that in another month or two if I continue on this dry spell," I said with a chuckle. "Man. What the hell was up with those glasses you had on? And you can't ride a bike, dude. What the hell?" I said, going straight for his jugular.

"What do you mean? I looked bad ass," Mick said, laughing.

"Bad ass? Oh my gosh, Mick. You're crazy. You looked so ridiculous," I said.

"That was some secret squirrel shit. G got those glasses from the FBI and they had a camera inside them. I recorded all of you motherfuckers," he said proudly.

"Really? That was a camera? Oh wow! Very cool man," I said, shocked.

"Yeah, bitch. I'm like that guy... What's his name? 007's main man," he said, struggling to think of his name.

"Who, Q?" I said.

"Yup. That's me. Just call me Q, baby," Mick said.

"That's pretty funny. But you're not Q," I said, shaking my head in disbelief.

"So how did it go?" I asked.

"It went pretty good. We got a lot more information than if we didn't go. We couldn't get into the inside perimeter where you were at but we were able to get a ton of plates and photos of guys entering and leaving. It was cool."

"Who else was there?" I asked.

"Al, G and another dude you don't know. This was all G. He has a ton of experience running UCs and large investigations. He worked for major narcotics for years. You'll have to meet him soon. I'm trying to get him more involved because I don't know what the fuck I'm doing and Al is a piece of shit. We need G."

"Well, it was nice knowing you guys were out there but you need to be careful, man. I don't want one of these militia boys to snipe you. Although, they probably couldn't hit you the way you were swerving on that bike," I said, laughing.

"The swerve is all part of my tactical plan, baby," Mick said, laughing.

"Hey. We were all locked and loaded. Did you know that?" I asked.

"No. But one dude I saw had an AR slung with a mag inserted. So I assumed you guys were. Crazy motherfuckers," Mick said and we both chuckled. "Those bastards shoot at me, I'll bust a cap in their ass," Mick said in his best gangster tone.

It was a long debrief. Twenty-six handwritten pages that lasted hours, but neither Mick nor I cared. Two young officers not experienced enough to know any better, but we did know we were holding the only Golden Ticket in the game, *Charlie and the Chocolate Factory* style. A momentous achievement for the stagnant and dying intelligence agency, ATD, once heralded as the greatest local law enforcement intelligence agency in the country. An unparalleled win for the city and its controversial undercover program that had been smeared with bad press and litigation years prior. No other federal, state or local law enforcement agency knew what we knew or had access to the movement at our level. The program and the intelligence was so secret not even the rank and file within LAPD knew. Only the chosen few with the proper security clearance knew: four ATD investigators, one lieutenant, one captain, a single city council member, and the Chief of Police. Only they knew the militia movements, political targets, objectives, their mission, the recruiting effort, their training calendar and who the main movers and shakers were. Only they knew the Program had a source on the inside of the militia movement to monitor it all and it was me.

"Whocco! What up, man? Where you been, foo?" Oz said. I had been off playing militia man, a week on the beach, etc. and we hadn't seen each other in a while. I missed him. We were complete opposites but he made me laugh.

"What's up, Oz! How have you been?" I said, attempting my best version of his gangster dab handshake.

"We have to work on that," Oz said, shaking his head at my lack of rhythm, whiteness or a combination of both.

"No. No. Wait. Let's try it again. I got this," I insisted we try his handshake again.

"Na man. It's cool. I like your whiteness," Oz said as we both started cracking up.

"Last time I saw Nester he said your cousin is okay?" I asked.

"Yeah. He got shot in the ass. But he's cool," Oz said.

"Good. I'm glad he's okay," I said.

"I owe you man," he said.

"Yes you do and I'm going to collect," I said, putting my arm around his neck.

"Oh. Here we go. What you got, Whocco?" he asked.

"You told me that you don't bang anymore and you don't carry a strap," I whispered.

"Ahh man," he said, pushing me away. His eyes squinted, matching his laugh and smile. "I don't. That was different," he said.

"Bullshit. It's the same. It's all bangin'," I said.

"Naaa. That's different, man. That's me *familia*," he said.

"You said that you owe me. That's what I want. Let's shake on it. You know how good I am at that," I said, laughing, but it was a serious request knowing he was a man of his word.

"Not sure that I can do that, Whocco, and I know that you don't know how to shake. So you better pick something else," Oz said, laughing but serious.

"Yes you can. Life's about choices, my man," I said, trying to convince a gang banger to give up his pacifier.

"Easy for you to say, Whocco. You're white and not from the neighborhood," he said.

I started laughing, "If you didn't notice. I am the only white guy living and working in the neighborhood. I should be the one that's strapped!" I said.

"Crazy Whocco. I can't do it, man. But I feel you," he said. "Hey. Me and Nester are going to Tio's for lunch do you want to go?"

"No. I already told Lupe I'd meet her for lunch," I said.

"Are you trying to tap that, man? She's got a nice ass, but nobody can crack that," he said.

"No. It's not like that. We're just friends," I said.

"White men can be friends with women without trying to tap that ass?" he asked, seriously perplexed by my response.

"Yeah. Why? Mexicans can't?" I asked.

"Fuck no, man. Not unless she's three hundred pounds. And even then I don't know. Why do you think we got so many kids?" he said, laughing.

"You're stupid. Funny, but stupid," I said, just shaking my head at him.

"It's true, man. Just sayin'. You know I'm right!"

"I'll take your word for it. I have to go meet my friend for lunch. Who is a girl and whose ass I don't want to tap," I said, laughing, walking away towards the front of the store.

"She's got a penis or you're gay then, bro," Oz said, loudly laughing at his own statement. A customer turned and looked in his direction, but Oz was unapologetic as I continued to walk up to meet Lupe.

"Hey you. How are you? I ordered you your grilled cheese sandwich and chips," Lupe said, greeting me with a side hug.

"Ah, very nice of you. Thank you. How are you?" I asked.

"I'm well. Thank you for asking. It is so busy up front today. Crazy," she said, still with a smile on her face. "People are talking about us, you know. Has anyone asked you about me?"

"No. Not really," I said.

"You lie," she said. "Really? I swear. People have nothing better to do with their time than to gossip," she said to herself.

"Just Oz was giving me a hard time because he wanted to go to lunch today and I told him that I was going with you," I explained.

"Ahh. You should have gone with him. He likes you. What was he saying?" she asked, hesitantly, like she really wanted to know what he'd said.

"Just guy talk. Nothing bad, I promise," I reassured her.

"Tell me. It's okay. I want to know what he said," she said, playfully slugging me in my arm but then rubbing it because she felt bad.

"It was all good. Oz loves you but it's not important." Not wanting to tell her he'd said she had a nice ass that I wanted to *tap*.

"You're a brat. I hate you," she said, frustrated with my lack of response but knowing it was most likely best she didn't know.

Shift in the Tides

"Fools rush in where angels fear to tread."
Alexander Pope

The militia movement continued to grow like a weed and the more entwined I became. Deep rooted. The Western Marksman Group held true to its promise at the call-up offering operational training to any militia members and groups that wanted to attend. The violent side of the movement I'd thought was there but had yet to experience became evident quickly. Groups of militia men training on a regular basis in military and police tactics, fully armed. Learning how to attack and defend themselves against the country and law enforcement agents they claimed to love so much. They were training to defend themselves against me. Training to kill me and my fellow brothers and sisters.

Beep, beep, beep. 940-2222. An unusual page from JT. Code two.

"Hey JT, what's going on?" I asked.

"That was fast, kid. How's everything going?" he asked, being nice to me. A rarity.

"All good. What's up?" I asked again, impatient.

"I know it's not time for your quarterly training but we need to meet. Are you available this week?" he asked.

"I can meet in the morning, but I have to be at work by two," I said.

"You're working nights now?" JT asked, always in my business, but I ignored his question. "Let's meet at the usual place and I'll page you with the info," he said.

The next morning, I received the page indicating the room number of the hotel room. Fifth floor this time! Up the back stairwell making my way to the room. JT opened the door and to my surprise it was crowded. The entire training unit was there: JT, Jack, Jay, David, Samantha and two suits I didn't recognize. Something had to be up.

"Thirty-six. Come in," JT said, calling me by my *bird* identification number. I looked at Samantha to see if she would give me any clue as to what was going on, but I only received a half-smile.

"Hey, sorry about this but these two guys are with personnel and your name came up again. They need to drug test you," JT said.

"Seriously? Here?" I asked.

"Yup. Hey. Let's get everyone to step outside for a minute. This guy has to stay in the room with you. Sorry, but the rest of us will leave. He's not to ask you anything and don't give him your name," JT said, which made zero sense to me. How would my name come up if they didn't know it? Stupid, I thought, but not worth the argument.

"Sure," I said, entering the bathroom with one of the suits as the rest of the clan left the room.

"Another first for me. I've never been in a hotel bathroom with a guy assigned to watch me pee," I said, trying to make light of a very awkward situation, but he didn't get my humor, like most.

"They make you wear a suit to collect pee?" I asked, trying again to get the guy to crack a smile but my delivery came across poorly as he took my warm cup of pee. Still dehydrated, I thought.

"Please verify your program identification number on the label and that it is sealed," the man said in a robotic voice, refusing to make eye contact with me.

"Yes, sir. My apologies for the comments. I was just trying to add a little humor to an awkward situation," I said. The man nodded, not saying a word. Placed my urine in a brown paper bag and left. The gaggle of police personnel all re-entered the room struggling to find a place to sit or stand in the small hotel room stuffed with two double beds and a small coffee table.

Not the most ideal location for what I was assuming must be an important meeting.

"Here, take a seat and let me tell you what's going on," JT said, motioning towards the bed next to the wall air conditioning.

"No thanks. I'm good," I said, leaning up against the wall near the bathroom.

"Well. I know it's not time for our quarterly training but I did bring your mail if you want to go through it," JT said, handing me my mail. The envelope was full. A great month for mail, I thought. People must have missed me but I deferred the task, to everyone's surprise. The setting wasn't right for me. Privacy, over an audience.

"Steven. We can step out if you want to read your mail in private," Samantha said.

"No. It's okay. I'll wait, but thank you. Is someone going to tell me what's going on?" I said, looking around at the group for a response.

"We've heard a lot of chatter about your work," JT said.

"How is the new guy, Mick?" Jack asked.

"Great, love him. Why?" I said with an inquisitive but protective tone.

"He seems like he has one speed. It's not too much for you?" JT asked.

"No. Not at all. Why do you ask that?" I said, feeling a witch hunt was in play.

"Well, we heard about your health issue and we're worried that they're working you too hard," JT said, locking eyes with me. A look I recognized back from my training days where he would manipulate me and

227

break me down with Jedi mind tricks. It wasn't going to happen today. He just didn't know it yet. Yoda, he was no longer.

"No. That's not the case. So, is that the real reason I was drug tested again?" I said sarcastically, not liking the line of questioning or the mood of the room.

My question went unanswered but it was clear that they knew I knew.

"And Al. How is Al?" Danny asked in a soothing voice, trying to ease the tensions.

I paused before I answered. "Can we not play the game? Is this why you brought me here? To talk bad about my handlers? Because that's what it seems like to me," I said matter-of-factly.

"Nobody asked you your opinion. Just answer his question!" Jack said, sounding pissed, knowing that if he and I were to go wits to wits, he was unarmed.

Ignoring Jack's aggression and not wanting to throw Al under a bus even though it was deserved, I said, "Al? Al is Al."

"What's wrong with Al?" Danny quickly jumped in before Jack lost it.

"I didn't say anything was wrong with Al, Danny. I said Al is Al," I clarified.

There was a long pause until JT broke the silence. "Yeah. Well, there has been a change in your assignment."

I cut JT off mid-sentence, "No. I'm not changing assignments again, JT. I'm too deep," I said.

Jack, still steaming, lost it. "You don't talk to a Sergeant of Police like that. You don't make the rules and you will do what the fuck we tell you to do!"

"Jack? You're such an asshole," I said, shaking my head.

Jack stood up and started to walk in my direction. "Fuck you!" he yelled.

JT stopped him. "Enough! Both of you shut up." The tension in the 14 x 14 room was palpable. The air conditioner kicked on, sensing the heavy atmosphere.

"Relax. Everyone just relax. The change in your assignment is you have new handlers, Steven. That's it. Al was promoted and Claire is having some medical issues so she is going to completely step away from the case," JT said.

Dumbfounded. "Al was promoted? To what?" I asked.

JT ignored my question. "Mick will remain your handler but the Captain is bringing in G to take Al's place. G is a supervisor and has a lot of experience supervising major cases. You'll get to meet him soon."

"Yeah. I know who G is. I've heard some good things about him," I said.

"How would you know who G is? Have you met him?" JT asked.

"No. No, I haven't met him. But Mick has told me good things about him. That's what I meant," I said.

"About to say... If you have met him then we have a problem," JT said, still trying to catch me out.

"No. I've never met him, but I look forward to meeting him. Is he coming today?" I asked.

"No. We just wanted to meet with you first to tell you. He'll be in contact with you. Remember: we're your gatekeepers. Everything and all changes that concern you always come through us," JT said, puffing his chest out. Not literally, but the Mexican machismo snuck out.

"Okay. Is that it?" I asked, not understanding the big production for a simple change in handlers.

"What do you mean is that it? Do you have any questions?" Danny asked.

"No. I don't have any questions," I said, still not understanding why Al was not my handler. And he was promoted?

"Do you need anything from us?" Jay asked, trying to play nicely now. Jack was still steaming in the corner. Samantha playing the neutral game well.

"No. I'm good, Jay. Thanks for asking," I said, acknowledging what seemed like a sincere request. Jack and I were locked in a staring contest like two juveniles at a birthday party.

"Okay. Thanks for coming. See you in a couple weeks for quarterly training," JT said and we parted ways.

Western Marksman Association

The next night the Rainier Park, Denali Park, and San Fernando militias attended the Western Marksman Association, Jax's group. The meeting was being held at Ted's place located in a suburb of Orange County. Ted: Asian, late thirties, standing five foot nine, 185 pounds. Traditional light skin, hairless. Medium build. House was well kept. Think soccer mom's house, lacking the soccer mom. Bachelor of Science and Master degrees, engineering from University of Southern California proudly framed and hanging in the hallway. World War II and other history books lined a bookshelf on two sides of his house. A small rat dog yipping constantly. Annoying and didn't fit his profile.

"Welcome everyone to our meeting. For those of you that don't know me, my name is Jax. Yes, it's my real name and my mother did love me," Jax said jokingly but didn't get the ice breaker response he anticipated. "We don't have an agenda tonight like we normally do but we just wanted to get everyone together and tell you a little bit about us, our mission and of course to get to know each other," Jax continued, grandstanding for the Denali Park and the San Fernando Groups who had never attended one of their meetings before.

"We meet once a week and train every other weekend. Any of our members can invite anyone to the open portion of our meetings which lasts approximately one hour. After the open meeting all non-members are adjourned and just our members meet in private. Most of our members do not attend the open portion of the meeting for security purposes. We do not talk about black helicopters, implanted chips, Russians, conspiracy crap of any sort. Our mission is to train and prepare any like-minded groups or individuals that are down for the cause. If you want a soapbox group, we're not it. If you want to talk about anything but training or preparing we're not the group for you. I don't mean to be blunt but I just don't want to waste anyone's time," Jax said, looking around at our group for a response.

"How long have you guys been around?" Gary, the commander from the San Fernando militia, asked.

"Our group has been loosely together for over two years. We joined the Orange County group which had about ten to fifteen different groups

231

under its umbrella. The meetings just sucked. There was no structure, no training, no preparedness. Our members along with two other groups just got tired of it and we left. So much better doing our own thing. That's why we're not about talk. We're about action. That's the bottom line. Our mission is we will train any militia groups that want training," Jax said.

"What kind of training do you offer?" Gary asked.

"We specialize in operations: Desert Patrols and CQB (Close Quarter Battle). Tomorrow night, we're training at an indoor gun range nearby if you or your groups want to attend. We'll give you the info at the end of the night. The cost is $20. The owner is a buddy of mine and he lets us train there after they close. It's great training!" Ted said.

The meeting was short but had served Jax's purpose.

<u>G</u>

Our first meeting was all business. A formality to me. He was just another handler I had to be on guard with. A victim of Al, JT, Jack, Claire, as a matter of fact the entire group's bullshit and games. I saw G as the next pawn in a game of chess the Department was seemingly playing and I was on my fourth game of checkers. G. A thick build unlike my small frame. Clean-cut white man, six feet, 210lbs of muscle. The stereotypical cop selected by the LAPD forty years ago. His biceps were as large as my thighs, but not in a bodybuilder way. Well spoken. Professional. Calming demeanor that exuded confidence and transparency. A handshake, firm, but not crushing, looking into your eyes. When G shook my hand for the first time, it reminded me of stories my grandfather used to tell. Back when he said that a man's handshake was his bond, his word. A brief look into a

232

man's soul that I should never take lightly. Absent attorneys, contracts, and lawsuits for lack of fulfillment. A time when a man shook your hand and said he was going to do something; he did it at all costs. G had that lost handshake of confidence my grandfather spoke of. I don't know why I thought that, but I knew.

"Tell me about tonight's event, Steven," G asked after we'd gone through the formalities.

"We're going to an indoor shooting range in Orange County. They're closing down the range to the public at 8 and we start at 8:15. Jax's group is hosting it and I think we're doing basic firearms training. But I'm not sure," I said.

"Do you know if Ted and Chip are also going?" G asked.

I was impressed he knew the members by name.

"I believe they are. But I'm not sure," I said, sitting up a little straighter.

"Who's going from your group?" he asked.

"I know Jeff and Tom are going for sure, but I don't know about the others," I said.

"Kelly normally doesn't work tonight. She's not going with Jeff?" he asked.

My face must have shown something.

"He knows everyone, man! He's like *Rain Man* on crack," Mick said, laughing and shaking his head at G's seemingly photographic memory.

G remained all business, ignoring Mick's comments. "What's your plan for tonight?" he asked.

233

"What do you mean? I'm going to go to the meeting and then when I'm done I'll call you guys for a debrief. Who has the on call?" I asked.

"I don't operate like that, Steven. We're going to do things a little differently now that I'm in charge of the case," G said, but not in a confrontational way.

"Okay. Like what?" I asked.

"First of all, your safety is my number one priority. I spoke with your parents and I promised them that I would do everything in my power to keep you safe. The days of you going to meetings or training without back-up are over," G said.

The effect of his words at that moment I am at a loss to describe. My eyes well up as I relive that moment today. Powerful. A moment burned into timelessness.

"What do you mean? How are you going to do that?" I asked. This conversation and G had just got real to me.

"Anytime you go anywhere unless you tell me otherwise Mick and I will be nearby as your back-up. If anything goes south, we'll coordinate with the local police, letting them know that we have a friendly inside. And we'll come get you," G said.

Mick nodded, adding, "You can bet your fucking ass we will!" His eyes turned into that 1,000-mile stare. Intense. No militia man would want to see it.

"Seriously? You guys are going to go to all of my meetings and training?" I asked, not sure if G understood the commitment he'd just made.

"Yes. Unless you tell me otherwise. We will be there and if we can't make it I'll have someone else there that I trust to protect you. I can't protect you from my couch," G confirmed. "Back to you and tonight. We're going to start working together and filling in these intelligence gaps. Phase No. 1 – We need to build out profiles on every single one of these guys, three layers deep. Do you know what I mean by that?"

"No sir. I do not," I said, showing him respect. My instincts told me it was well deserved.

"Layer one. The basics. You get us any tangible intelligence and Mick and I can fill in most of the gaps via computer runs or other sources. We'll verify that information through you. Where they work. Families. Registered cars. Weapons. Finances. Restaurants. Grocery stores. Dry cleaning. Banks. Bars. Hobbies. That kind of stuff," he said.

"Got it. What's layer two?" I asked. Intrigued.

"Layer two is their safety net. Think of who they would contact if they were in trouble. Where would they go? Second home? Favorite vacation spot they know well. Camp grounds. Friends' houses. Parents, uncles, aunts. Storage facility. Everyone has that one place or person they'll turn to when they're in trouble. We'll find out who and where that is. Make sense?" G asked.

"Yes sir. It does," I said as a bigger picture, a more focused duty, began to form in my head.

"Layer three is all you," he said.

"What do you mean?" I asked.

"Layer three is the stuff that only your best friend or your wife would know. The bones in their closet. Dig up their bones. The crosses they carry, but don't speak of freely. Do you understand?"

"I do but I don't think I can get there. These guys are worse than cops. They don't trust anyone," I said.

"It will come. Trust me. I've seen it before. Just be patient and keep doing what you're doing. You're good," G said with confidence. "We'll build out the profiles of these guys and develop threat assessments on everyone and each group. The threat assessment will determine where our investigation goes. That's a high-level view. Do you understand?"

"I get it," I said, shaking my head, processing what seemed like an even greater feat. "I like it. Let's do it," I said, excitedly nodding.

"Fuck yeah! Let's do this, boys," Mick said, louder than he should have.

"Tonight. I like Jax and Ted. They seem to be the leaders with a little bit of bark. I just don't know if it's all bark or if there's a bite," I said.

"Okay. Mick, what do you think?" G asked.

"Yup. That's my pick too," Mick said.

"It's settled then. They're your targets tonight. Also Gary, the commander of the San Fernando cell. If he attends and you have the opportunity to get close to him, I need your opinion on him. The Feds have him high on their target list, but I don't see it. Let me know what you think," G said.

"Will do," I said, focused.

"Here is how I work on debriefs. Page me as you normally have been when you clear. Mick or I will debrief with you any day and time you want. But you decide. If you're too tired after a meeting or have other plans we'll debrief the next morning. I would prefer that we debrief immediately after the event because it's the most accurate information, less time for memory dump. My point is, we're a team, but you are the main character. We'll debrief on your schedule. Questions? Do you need anything from us?" G asked.

"No, sir. I'm good for now," I said.

G. I would come to call him G-Man. A coined term referencing an FBI agent dating back to the 1930s. The Al Capone days. G wasn't a big fan of my extended name for him by definition alone. G was a cop's cop and had supervised some of the most elite units LAPD had to offer. A true leader. A supervisor who led from the trenches but was comfortable amongst the suits and the brass. He was brighter than most of them and they knew it. G, like most city cops, wasn't too fond of FBI agents who couldn't investigate their way out of a paper sack. College boys with fancy suits who threw federal money at the local cop's investigations, eventually standing in the front row at the press conference taking credit. Pompous. Believing they were above the local cop in the pecking order of law enforcement. G tolerated them when forced, that's why my extended name for him was so beautiful. G-Man.

Guns R Us Training

Seventeen militia men and one militia woman with a white flower in her hair showed up for the training which was located at Jax's buddy's indoor gun range. His group had been training at this facility for over a year. Tonight, Jax and Ted were running the training. It felt like an in-service LAPD training to me, less of the grab-assing. Organized. Safety first mentality. It was obvious they both had significant experience in not only handling weapons but in firearms instructing. After a safety briefing we were broken up into three groups and given our assignments. The groups rotated stations every forty minutes.

"Here are the groups. I tried to keep units together with a few exceptions. Steven, I put you with the Cypress group and Gary, you'll be with Denali to even things out. Get your gear ready and be at your stations in five," Jax announced to the group.

I couldn't have written the script any better. The Cypress group had been associated and training with Jax and Ted's group for over a year. I saw it as an opportunity. Not only to start to build out the Cypress group and their capabilities but also to check some boxes in the phase two category for Jax and Ted. My targets for the night.

I was excited for the training. By design not coincidence, my gear included a recent purchase of a 9mm pistol. A Barretta 92fs. Same as the duty weapon I was issued and trained on in the police academy. For the shotgun, a Remington, 12 gauge. Borrowed. My greatest concern of the night was the firearms training itself. All LAPD officers are trained to manipulate, stand and shoot a pistol the same way. Methodical. Robotic. Identifiable. Weaver shooting stance not used by most gun enthusiasts. A shooting technique developed by Los Angeles County Deputy Sheriff Jack Weaver. Widely adopted by LAPD in the 1950s. Drawing and exhibiting the pistol. Four distinct positions not used by civilians.

Position No. 1	Ready Position – weak hand covers your belt as your gun hand obtains a solid grip, finger alongside the holster.
Position No. 2	Close contact position – Draw your pistol elbow tucked at your side at a 90-degree angle. Barrel of the pistol canted, 45-degree

238

	angle, pointed slightly upward, finger alongside the frame.
Position No. 3	Low ready position – Punch the weapon out, acquiring a two-handed grip, Weaver stance. Weapon at a 45-degree angle. Finger alongside the frame. Assess left right center.
Position No. 4	On target. Acquire your target finger on the trigger. Fire. Assess left right center. Tactical reload. Assess again.

Speed reloads. A process to reload your pistol quickly. LAPD taught the technique very specifically: grab a loaded magazine from your gun belt while simultaneously ejecting the empty magazine in the pistol, reloading it and back on target. Detailed to the point that only two fingers were allowed to grip the magazine removing it from your belt. Adding the index finger after the magazine was removed to guide it into the magazine well of the pistol. The angle of the pistol when the magazine release button was hit with your thumb. It had to be your thumb. Then tapping the bottom of the magazine with your weak hand to ensure the magazine is seated fully in the pistol before hitting the slide release button to chamber a live round.

This applied to everything. Shooting on the move. Tactical reloads. Pistol malfunction clearances. LAPD officers are clones. Put me on a firing line with a militia man and ask anyone in the know. They will tell you every time that I am LAPD trained. A top shot in my class. One of the few who qualified expert. *How do I unlearn or hide my engrained habits? I was thinking.*

Group No. 1   Rainier militia – Tom, Jeff, Kelly, Mike, Steven, and Harold

Group No. 2   Denali militia – Jason, David, Kevin, Johnny, Ralph and
              Gary. Commander of the San Fernando militia.

Group No. 3   Cypress militia – Billy, Richard, Bob, Jack, Mark, and
              myself.

Station No. 1 – A class on firearm care and manipulations.

- Pistol maintenance – breakdown, clean, inspect and oil a pistol.
- Shotgun maintenance – breakdown, clean inspect and oil a shotgun.
- Tactical and speed reload manipulations.

Station No. 2 – Shotgun. Proper grip and stance. Standard load and unload. Tactical loading. Slinging the shotgun. Transitioning from shotgun to pistol. Malfunctions.

Course of Fire:

At the sound of the beep…

- Fire four rounds. One round each. Center mass on the left target, center mass on the right target.
- Complete a tactical reload with two rounds.
- Fire two additional rounds to the head. Head shot on the left target; head shot on the right target.
- Sling your shotgun and transition to your pistol moving to cover. Engage targets three and four with a failure drill (two shots to the body and one to the head).
- Holster.

240

Station No. 3 – Handgun. Proper grip and stance. Marksmanship. Trigger pull. Sight alignment. Trigger reset. Tactical reloads. Speed reloads. Point shooting. Shooting on the move. Multiple target engagement. Malfunctions.

Course of Fire:

At the sound of the beep…

- Six shots – two left, two right, left head shot, right head shot.
- Speed reload while moving to cover.
- Two shots – left head shot; right head shot.

Our group started at Station No. 3. Billy was the main character. Team leader, not by title. By performance. Focused. Expert marksman. High quality gear. Laser focus. Clutch under pressure. The men responded to him. Humble and soft spoken. Unassuming, which worried me more.

"Okay, boys. We're going to finish with a little competition. Course of fire, timed. Ring score. Who wants to go first?" Jax announced to our group, looking at his watch.

"I'll go first," Billy volunteered, showing no fear. He's good, I thought, scoring a 77 out of 80, but I could beat him.

"Great job, Billy! That's going to be tough to beat," Jax said, showing his target.

Richard went next, scoring a 65/80. He missed a head shot. Followed by Bob, 50/80, missing both head shots. Jack shot well with a 72/80. Mark crapped the bed, scoring 42/80. I was up next. My ego and the competitor in me wanted to win. But I knew winning the competition might hurt me. But besides that I wanted to show well. Just not too well.

"At the sound of the beep, complete the course of fire. Shooter, are you ready?" Jax asked me.

I nodded.

"At the sound of the beep," Jax said, pushing the button.

Beep! I drew my pistol. Fired shots 1–2. Both shots struck the ten ring. Switching to the right target I fired shots 3–4, striking the ten ring. Back to the left target, shot 5, head shot. It was a hit. Back to the right target, shot 6, head shot. Another hit. My target was clean, moving to the speed reload and my final two shots. Moving to cover, I fumbled removing the fresh magazine from my belt, hitting the magazine release button on my pistol. The fresh magazine dropped to the floor, leaving me with an empty pistol. I stopped.

"Keep going," Jax yelled. The buzzer went off and I didn't finish the course of fire.

"Steven! You can't stop. Grab another magazine. Pick that one up and get in the gun fight," Jax continued. All stuff that I knew but was too soon for Steven.

"Steven… nice shooting, man. I think you would have had me," Billy said, relieved.

"Maybe. If I didn't have to do that reload," I said.

"I practice speed reloads when I watch television. You should try it. It works," Billy said.

"Really? While you're watching television?" I asked.

"I do. I even practice at night in the dark. That's even harder," Billy said.

"Good advice. Thank you," I said.

242

Our group moved onto Station No. 1, firearm care and manipulations, taught by Ted. My plan was to sit back, listen and learn. Ask an occasional question even if I knew the answer.

"Welcome, boys. I think everyone knows me here except for Steven so I'll shorten my spiel. I've been a certified NRA instructor for over ten years and I'm also a certified armorer. That's all I got. So, I hope I know how to teach this class by now," Ted said and the boys laughed. "Steven. What's your experience with guns?" he asked me.

"He can fucking shoot," Richard chimed in and answered for me.

"Oh. Okay. Did you beat Billy?" Ted asked.

I started to answer but Mark cut me off.

"No. But he was *clean* until he fucked up the mag change. Otherwise, he would have taken him down," Mark said.

"Nice work. Okay let's get into it," Ted said and he started the class. There was no doubt Ted was an NRA instructor. Very thorough and knowledgeable in his presentation. He knew all of the correct terminology and provided full explanations on the pistol operations and maintenance. Ted moved into pistol manipulations next, which is where I was most frightened due to my LAPD training.

"Steven, I've taught this class to these guys a few times so they know it. Is there something that you don't know or want to learn?" Ted asked.

"You can teach him speed reloads," Mark said with a grin. Everyone laughed.

"Good point, Mark," I said.

Ted, having trained the Cypress group over the last year, gave our group a pass for the remainder of the class. Lucky for me. We just sat around and shot the shit for the next thirty minutes. Then our group moved onto the last stage. Shotguns. Not my favorite weapon. I always hated it but I prefer it for home defense. Just point in the general area and pull the trigger. Chances are you will hit your target depending on the distance. I always saw it as a weapon that didn't require much skill. The last stage went well but no one really stood out as if that were their weapon of choice. The night ended with a debrief by Jax and Ted asking for training feedback and/or future requests. Everyone was ecstatic with the training. How could they not be? Here these militia boys and one lady were receiving top tier firearms training that law enforcement officers rarely received. All for the bargain price of $20. Who could beat that?

My objectives for the night had been achieved. Jax and Ted had both warmed up to me and I'd showed well. Like a horse prancing around before the big race. Intel gathering, a few paces forward on both targets. Nothing earth shattering, but the turtle wins the race in this game. Gary, the commander of the San Fernando militia, newly awarded a place on the FBI militia target list, had eluded me. Next time, I thought. But from what I saw he wasn't a gunslinger. Uncomfortable with a weapon. Not technical. Not fluid. His gear sucked. He looked like a monkey fucking a football negotiating those stages. I didn't know why he'd made the FBI's target list, but he wasn't an *operator*.

Debrief

G-Man and Mick were both nearby covering the winds of the shooting range as promised. My safety net in place. We met up that night and it was a different type of debrief than I was used to. The old style of me

244

regurgitating everything I could and my handlers writing feverishly remained. It was the engagement after that. Mick and G-Man asked me questions about what I'd seen. Heard. Line by line, we would go over the notes. *What do you mean by this? Did he mention anyone else when he was talking about this? Who was around when he said that? Do you think Jax could have been referring to this?* No longer a one-way pipeline of information wandering aimlessly in the abyss. G-Man, Mick and I were laser focused. Equally dedicated to the cause. G-Man and Mick giving up their lives, family and friends as did I, all to get a handle on this movement. We were shooting fish in a barrel. They would tell me which fish to target and I would pick them off one by one. As an added bonus, a few fish would miraculously flop into our barrel unexpectedly and I would plug them too.

Night Out

Date night! Jean. A local girl. Well, sort of. We'd met at the YMCA. A former gymnast who taught aerobics classes there for extra cash. I would go there for an occasional workout to keep my militia man cardio up to par, stress levels in check, and my testicular pain at a minimum. She was a Texas transplant chasing the Hollywood dream. Working as a cocktail waitress in between acting lessons and side gigs. A rare find in my neighborhood. Long blond hair, medium height, thin build. She didn't fit in, but neither did I for that matter. Maybe that's why we hit it off? It sure wasn't my biceps.

Liz was weighing on my mind heavily leading up to the date. I was excited to move on, but nervous. I didn't want to go through all of the first date questions, especially in my current situation.

Jean had asked if I wanted to join her and some friends who were going out for dinner and drinks at a new restaurant. A group date filled with Hollywood dream chasers. My excitement level was low, but I went with the flow. Jean was dressed to the nines! Isn't nine one short of ten? I never understood that phrase, until I looked up its origin – a Scottish poet, which explains my confusion; I was never fond of poetry. Black high heels with knee-high stockings, a matching mini skirt showing her toned thighs. Black tube top. Her stomach muscles playing peek a boo under a jacket.

I didn't recognize her when she was walking down a short flight of stairs to join me. "Hi. How are you?" she said with a huge smile, giving me a hug. Caress soap smell. My hand grasping her around the small of her back as we hugged. I felt a back muscle on this girl.

"Wow. You look different. I mean in a good way," I stumbled.

"Thank you. I think," she said, giggling.

"I mean... Your hair, make-up. Clothes. I'm not used to seeing you like this," I stumbled again.

"I guess I clean up good. Thank you," she said, letting me off the hook.

Financially, I was also nervous. Money was always tight and I knew after tonight I would be eating ramen for a couple of weeks. Dinner was awesome though. Italian joint, with a rooftop table and views overlooking downtown. Spritz for drinks. Italian style. The conversation was fascinating and non-stressful. They were all transplants from different worlds. Everyone chasing what seemed like an impossible dream.

Struggling, but doing it their way. Free, but at a price. We talked about life. Dreams. Struggles. Friends. Work. Absent were conspiracy theories, op-sec protocols, weapons, preparedness for the world's inevitable end, snitches, or explosives. It was refreshing.

"Hey. I want to go dancing! Do you guys want to go to a club?" Jean asked with enthusiasm.

"I'm sorry. Do you dance? Do you want to go, Steven?" Jean said, forgetting that we were on a date, putting her hand on my thigh and asking with her huge smile.

"Sure. Let's go," I said.

"Can you dance?" she asked again.

"Of course I can dance," I said, laughing.

Jean laughed, trying to process if I was telling the truth or being sarcastic.

The group was excited as we headed out to the club located about twenty miles outside of Los Angeles in a neighboring town. The line was long. It was ladies' night! Standing in the back of the line. Impatient. Wishing I had my badge to buzz security, forgoing the long line. A professional courtesy all but lost today.

"Lacy. Let's see if we can get us in," Jean said.

"There goes our dates, Steven. We're screwed," a young lad named Chad, Lacy's date, said, putting his arm around me.

Lacy, Jean plus one on the hotness scale, was dumb as a stump but hilarious. Lacy and Jean began their journey holding hands along the way, laughing, working what God had given them as they headed towards the front of the line. Cat-calls from the men along the way. Women sizing them up as they walked by until they disappeared out of my sight. Ten minutes later I saw Jean waving the remainder of the group up to the front of the line. Amazing; these girls were good. Women. A man's weakness and strength…

We were lucky to find a table. It was in the back of the club some distance from the dance floor but I was pleased with the location. First order of business: drinks. I ordered a club soda with a lime. My pseudo-Vodka tonic. After a group toast, Chad pulled out a vial containing cocaine and chalked out two lines on the table.

"Anyone need a pick me up?" he asked, snorting the first line. He passed a cut-down straw to Lacy. Lacy snorted the second line as Chad chalked out a few more lines. Jean was up next.

"Do you mind?" she asked me and I shook my head no. Jean snorted the line, closing her eyes, tilting her head back and whipping her nose like a professional, letting out a huge scream of what I could only assume was euphoria. She turned to me, offering me the straw. I shook my head, taking the straw from her hand and passing it along to Mary. Mary followed my lead and declined. Ted, her date, also declined. Back to Chad, who snorted the last line.

I was disappointed. Shocked. How could such a beautiful woman, functioning at a high level intellectually, caring about her body, snort cocaine? Nothing added up to me anymore. What a shame. Anger started to build inside me but I didn't understand why. Fuck this girl. Hollywood wannabe. Jean's path was predestined, she just didn't know it. Drug addiction, false Hollywood promises in exchange for sex. I'd seen it many times. As the group headed to the dance floor, she grabbed my hand and gave me a kiss, moving down to my neck. The devil in my left ear fighting with the angel in my right. A man's needs, blinding hotness and sexuality,

248

in a knock-down drag-out fight with my morals and ethics. A clear winner came into view quickly when we reached the dance floor. I saw my Aunt Shirley. She was dancing with a guy and he was not my Uncle Dan. Now that's a *pickle.*

I stopped in shock. Jean was pulling me towards the dance floor. Me resisting like my dog when we arrive at the groomers. I mouthed to her that I had to go to the restroom. She removed her jacket, handing it to me and revealing the most toned body I have ever seen on a woman. Time froze. I watched my Aunt Shirley dance with the guy free as a bird. Moving sensually. Unlike the Aunt Shirley I knew. A mother of three. Always dressed modestly in a long flowing dress. Hair in a bun or ponytail, no make-up, just trying to get through the day when you have a husband that works and you're a stay home mom raising three kids with no time to yourself.

We locked eyes, staring at each other, both of us in shock. My physical appearance was different – beard and long hair – but there was no mistaking either of us. My Aunt Shirley had known me since birth. I shook my head slightly to her, signaling not to approach me. But she most likely thought that it was in response to my disapproval of her dancing with a guy who was not my uncle. Figures, the one time I didn't perform any op-sec protocols. I had no idea the layout of the club except the front door. My temporary safe haven was returning Jean's jacket to our table followed by a restroom visit to come up with a plan. Standing in a puddle of urine on the floor of the men's bathroom stall. At least it wasn't mine, I thought. Drunk guys never aim well or seem to care. I had my smoking hot date snorting lines of cocaine dancing on the dance floor with my Aunt Shirley with some guy that wasn't my uncle. And mister elite undercover officer is hiding out in the men's bathroom stall, standing in piss not knowing what to do. *This is some elite undercover shit, Mac*, I thought to myself. *How can a night out turn bad so quickly ... WTH?* I stood in the puddle of urine for fifteen minutes processing before I left the restroom. Jean was standing at our table looking for me when I returned.

"Hey! There you are. Let's go!" she yelled, riding her cocaine high. Her pupils were blown out.

"Hey. I don't want to ruin your night. This isn't my scene. I'm going to take off. Do you have a ride?" I asked, laying forty dollars down on the table. Jean nodded, sucking the last of her cocktail through the cocaine-laced straw. She took the money, placed it in her jacket pocket, gave me a kiss on the cheek and bounced back to the dance floor screaming and flailing her arms in the air.

I ended the night alone on my couch. Jean, dressed in her heels, knee-high stockings, mini skirt, tube top, cocaine-laced nose, was replaced with a Big Gulp, sweet tarts and *Ferris Bueller's Day Off*. The movie I'd rented at the new Blockbuster store by my apartment. Maybe Aunt Shirley was a secret agent too, I thought? Our paths didn't cross again for several years after I was out from under the sheets. We never spoke of it and she's now married to the dude on the dance floor.

29 Palms

The Western Marksman Association was hosting a robust weekend training event near the 29 Palms military base. The best way to describe it… it could be hell. Jax had handed out the tentative training schedule the prior meeting. I'm not sure robust fully describes the training event. By far the longest and most advanced training event that I have seen the militia attempt to pull off. Half day training on Friday with night operations. Full day of training on Saturday with night operations, finishing up with a Sunday morning operation followed by a debrief. A marathon militia training event that will go down as legendary within the movement.

Mick, G-Man and myself met at the Denny's the Thursday before to discuss the weekend's plan. Denny's was an easy meet location for me and besides I loved the Yankee pot roast. I arrived first that day. I gave them the all-clear sign when I saw them arrive.

"Scoot over, sugar lips," Mick said, giving me a shove across the torn bench seat.

"Why are you sitting here? Go sit over there next to your boss," I said.

"I want to sit next to you today, baby," Mick said, putting me in a headlock and kissing me on the forehead.

"Get off me. Why?" I asked.

"Because I love you, baby and I'm tired of his ass," Mick said, laughing.

"Well get out and you sit on the inside so I can leave if I have to," I said.

"Are you two finished with your bickering over where you're going to sit, so we can get to work?" G-Man asked, knowing that if he didn't step in Mick and I would continue our bickering for an additional ten minutes.

Mick and I just laughed, realizing G-Man was all business today.

"Hey, I have to go to the bathroom. Can you order me my usual if she comes? See, Mick, you would've had to get out if you were sitting here," I said.

"Well, I forgot you have a bladder of a six-year-old girl," Mick fired back as G-Man shook his head, trying to keep us on point.

"Okay, children, are we ready to get to work?" G-Man asked when I got back.

"Yes, boss. Sorry. I only have one thing new. Kelly called me and wants to know if she can catch a ride with me because Jeff isn't going," I said.

"Is she *jonesing* on you?" Mick asked immediately.

"Well … do you blame her. I look pretty damn sexy as a militia man," I said, laughing.

"Did she say why Jeff wasn't going?" G-Man asked, ignoring mine and Mick's childish comments.

"Yeah, she said that Jeff was having work issues over his social security card and taxes. I guess he hasn't paid his taxes in years like most of these militia boys and his work is pissed, but he won't give them his social security card. She said that they're most likely going to fire him and they've been fighting a lot," I said.

"She didn't mention any type of threats towards his work did she?" G-Man asked.

"No. She didn't. I don't think Jeff would do that but you never know a man's breaking point," I said.

"We need to monitor that. We can't have him snapping and going to shoot up his place of employment," G-Man said.

"I agree. Do you want to set up on him this weekend? See where he goes and make sure he doesn't do anything stupid?" Mick asked.

"Depends. Steven, did they mention anything about security patrols during this training?" G-Man asked.

"They did mention they were going to have some security protocols in place but didn't tell me what they were. I don't need any support on this one. It's in the middle of the desert. You can't cover me there. I got it," I said.

"I don't want to leave you blind out there," G-Man insisted.

"Much appreciated, boss, but it's too dangerous out there. I don't think there's any way to cover me from the ground," I said.

"How about air support at a high altitude?" he asked.

I started to laugh but G-Man was serious. "Seriously. I got it, boss," I said, making eye contact with him followed by a nod.

"Okay. Let me make a phone call. I'll be right back," G-Man said, leaving Mick and I sitting next to each other like a loving couple.

"Well? Get your ass over there," Mick said, louder than he should, pushing me.

"I thought you said you love me, baby?" I said, sliding closer to Mick.

"I do love you, baby!" Mick said, grabbing me once again and giving me a bear hug.

"Get off me," I said, laughing as I sat on the other side of the booth. G-Man returned fifteen minutes later to me sitting in his seat eating my Yankee pot roast.

"You two lovebirds didn't want to sit next to each other any more? Thanks for waiting," G-Man said.

"Sorry, boss. Come back over here, baby," Mick said with a mouth full of food.

"Okay, listen. I called Ten-David and he agreed to have a team on standby with a helo this weekend to cover you. If anything goes south and you can't get out, find a hole and put on your orange hunter's hat when you hear the bird. The orange hunter's hat will tell them that you're the friendly. They won't shoot you," G-Man said.

"Oh, that's comforting. Who's Ten-David?" I asked.

"The LAPD SWAT commander, you dumbass," Mick said, not missing a bite of his food.

"He's a friend," G-Man said. "Mick. The Captain didn't approve overtime to set up a crew on Jeff this weekend," he added.

"Are you serious? What the fuck. I say we do it anyway. We need to cover this guy. What happens if he goes postal? How would that look that they didn't want to pay us overtime? This place is incredible," Mick ranted.

"We can't work it off-duty as much as I want to. Let me work on it and I'll let you know," G-Man said to Mick.

I left work early the next day and met Kelly at my place. It was strange seeing a woman with a white flower in her hair load an SKS rifle into the back of my car. She seemed so *girly* to me. A puzzle or maybe a riddle that occupied my mind from time to time. Like the television game show *Jeopardy*. Coming up with the answer framed as a question.

The three-hour car ride went quickly. Kelly was in a talkative mood and, unlike any woman I had ever traveled with, never asking for a *potty* break. She talked about Jeff, the movement, and the training, but rarely focused on herself. Selfless, lost and stuck with a man that she didn't love. Her situation was sad to me. Men leave these situations. Why do women stay? Was the movement really Kelly's fight? Or was it just the only bond she had left with Jeff? We arrived on time, turning off the freeway and heading across the open desert on a dirt road not often traveled. Dirt and rocks went flying through the air as we headed towards our final destination, the base of a hill, not quite reaching mountain status. The dirt kicked up in the air alerted the camp to our arrival. Camp was already set up when we arrived. Camouflaged shades, E-Z Up-style tents along with desert camouflaged netting to hide our camp from the air. Shooting lanes with paper targets off in the distance. Makeshift fire pit encircled with camping chairs. Tents sporadically positioned near vehicles parked in a circle. Circling the wagons.

"Hello, everyone. Welcome and thank you for coming. I want to go over this weekend's training to make sure everyone is on the same page. But first I want to introduce you to Brian. Brian is going to be helping out with the training this weekend. He's a former Army Ranger Special Forces. He knows his shit so listen to him," Jax said, opening the briefing.

Brian. Physically, think Poncherello from *CHiPs* without the gleaming smile. Black, middle part feathered hair. Medium height. Medium build. Dark eyes. Hispanic. Quiet type. Uncomfortable as the center of attention. Brian handled the safety brief with Jax and Ted adding color commentary. A brief that notified everyone what was determined the hot zone, loaded weapons or live fire. The shooting course and the direction of fire. The rules of engagement if we encountered any unfriendlies. The escape and evasion plan if the government were to come crashing in on our party. Law enforcement-style briefing covering every detail. Well planned and well thought out. Brian went on to go over the security plan. Billy set out boom mics along the single road leading to our camp as one early warning sign of any intruders. Impressive and very sophisticated, I thought. Jax told everyone to have all their gear ready and

255

report to the firing line in twenty minutes to sight in our rifles. Eight of us at a time lined up in a straight line. Brian standing behind us acting as the range officer.

"Everyone on the line. Let's clean it up. Dress right," Brian said, referring to the military term, not fashion. Everyone looked to their right and adjusted the line, ensuring it was straight.

"Take a prone position," Brian yelled. The line of militia men and one woman dropped to their stomachs.

"Make ready for live fire," Brian yelled, which caught me off guard. That phrase was exactly what LAPD officers say at our training events.

"Fire five rounds on your target. Slow fire at your pace. On my command," Brian yelled.   "Is there anyone on the line not loaded and ready to fire?" he asked. Another LAPD phrase announced at our monthly qualifications. "The line is hot. Fire," Brian said as gunshots rang out. Dust went flying up in the air with each shot, affecting our vision.

The weaponry displayed on the firing line varied immensely. The weapon of choice was the AR-15 style weapon. Many of the rifles were tricked out. Bipods, scopes, three-point slings. Others rifles I saw were the FN FAL – 308 rifle. The Rugar mini-14. At the bottom of the list, the Rainier militia were all equipped with SKS rifles with iron sights.

Jax and Ted were the adjunct instructors inspecting each militia man's target to see if the rifle sights had to be adjusted. My grouping was surprisingly tight for never firing this rifle before. Straight out of the box at 100 yards. I hit the target four out of five times. The grouping, low and left with only one flyer. *This rifle may look like a relic but that's impressive*, I thought.

"Nice shooting, Steven. I like your grouping. Let's move you up two clicks and one to the right," Jax said, patting me on the back after he adjusted my sights. Kelly's target was next to mine. She had one hit with four flyers.

"Listen up! Five more shots. Slow fire at your own pace on my command. Everyone make ready for live fire," Brian announced to the line.

The next volley of shots rang out on Brian's command. I focused. Controlling my breathing. Lining my sights up. Breath in, exhale halfway, hold. Slow squeeze of the trigger. Surprise trigger break. *Bang!* I stayed focused on my sights, not looking at my target; releasing the trigger slowly until I felt it reset. Hold there. Continue my breath. Exhale halfway. Hold. Slow trigger pull, surprise trigger break. *Bang!* I repeated this process until my five rounds were fired.

"Steven. Nice shooting, man. And that's with iron sights! Tell me what you think. We can move your sights one more click to the right if you want, but I think you're good," Jax said, handing me his binoculars for me to see my hits. Five hits. All technically center mass but not my best grouping. I was nervous and I couldn't control my heart rate.

"No. I'm good, Jax. That will work," I said, handing back his binoculars.

"Okay. You're done. Make sure you're unloaded and you'll be on break until everyone else gets dialed in," Jax said.

The "B" team finished forty-five minutes later. A label based on my assessment of the different qualifying groups. Nothing official. The "A" team, Jax and his peeps, were up next. Top notch gear. All equipped with AR-15s, load-out vests, glass (scopes), and many had collapsing bipods mounted to the front of their rifles for stabilization. Brian gave the same commands. The second group began their slow fire. Five shots. Each team member examined their own targets and made their own adjustments to their rifles. Second volley. Five shots and they were done. All rifles were sighted in. It was quick compared to my group. Impressive. True marksmen.

Next on the agenda was a class taught by Brian. Desert patrol tactics. He drew out formations on a whiteboard detailing different movements. Skirmish lines. Attack formations, that kind of normal stuff for civilians. After a short break, Ted was up. He taught the group marksmanship and shooting platforms. Strong side, weak side, trigger control, sight picture. Shooting positions – prone, kneeling supported, kneeling unsupported, off hand, and standing. No need to look up these terms if you're not in the know. Know this... All advanced techniques.

The training sessions were over and we all broke for dinner. No gourmet meals tonight. No hot dogs or hamburgers roasting over the fire. No smores. This weekend's menu ... Meals Ready to Eat (MREs). The Department of Defense introduced the first wide production of MREs to our military in the 1980s. The meals varied and had been improved over the years and were widely used by our military troops during Operation Desert Storm. The militia were testing the MREs to determine if they were a viable food source for the movement. Three days of MREs; I don't recommend it. My choice tonight was chicken with rice. The dark brown package included: chicken (I think), rice, fruit, crackers with cheese spread, and a cookie. A cookie the likes of which I have never tasted or seen. Other options on the menu: Tuna with noodles, meatballs w/tomato sauce, pork with rice, corned beef hash, chicken or beef stew. The militia boys loved them! I don't know how. Breakfast, lunch and dinner. MREs. It was terrible and it clogged me up for three days.

"Who's ready for night ops? I can only take four guys," Randy said to the group.

Randy, a member of the Western Marksmen Group, lived nearby the military base. He and his son knew the area well from years of riding dirt bikes in the area. Jax, Ted, and Billy all got up out of their chairs assuming they were going.

"Steven. Do you want to go with us?" Jax asked, but I had no idea where they were going or what they were doing.

"Sure. What do I need?" I asked.

"Nothing. I got you," Jax said as we piled into Randy's truck. Randy and his son sat up front and the rest of us jumped in the bed of the truck. Jax, Ted and Billy had their full load-outs. Rifles slung and at the ready. I was armed with my pistol but had left my rifle behind following Jax's instructions. The moonlight was blocked by cloud cover. There was a chill in the air. It was dark and my stomach was trying to work out what it had done to me to deserve such punishment. Randy, blacked out, driving fast down the road, made a quick left, tossing me into Jax.

"Sorry! I almost missed the turn," Randy called out.

Turn on your damn headlights, I was thinking, *and you might be able to see. This isn't even a road!* The truck was swerving left, back right, hitting what I could imagine were huge holes in the desert floor. Holding on tight, the four of us were getting rocked but no one said anything. One particular swerve, my back slammed against the back of the truck bed. A sharp pain unlike anything I'd ever felt before.

"Randy! Slow the fuck down," Jax yelled, banging on the top of the cab.

Fifteen minutes later the truck came to a stop.

"Steven. Here's the deal. The military base is over that ridge," Jax said, pointing to a ridge that I couldn't really see. "The marines train over there all the time. After their training ops they don't police the range that well. They leave stuff behind because it's free to them. They don't care. But we can use it. Some nights we get some great stuff. Tracers, grenades, even mortars. We're going to go check it out and see if we can hit the jackpot," Jax said.

"Okay. What do you want me to do?" I asked.

"You don't have any night vision do you?" he asked.

"Night vision? No. I don't," I said.

"Okay. Just stay close to us. If you see something, call one of us over. Don't just pick it up – it could be a bomb," Jax said.

"A bomb? Really?" I asked.

"Well, not a bomb, bomb. But unexploded ordnance or a grenade that has explosives so just call us over before you pick anything up," he said confidently.

"No lights," Ted said, putting on his night vision. "Don't use your torch. If there are any night patrols or if anyone comes, our rally point is Randy's truck just over the ridge."

Jax, Billy and Ted all had night vision goggles. The four of us headed towards the ridge. Randy and his son stayed behind with our getaway vehicle. The hike to the crest of the ridge was longer than I thought. Just shy of two miles. The four of us rested on the crest. A slight breeze was blowing in my face. Brisk. Remnants of the desert in my eyes, teeth and ears. The moonlight freed from the clouds revealed the desert valley. It was beautiful. A brief moment of escape for me taking in God's creation of beauty. Compartmentalizing the three men to my right armed with 210 rounds of .223 ammunition, equipped with night vision, on a mission to go steal explosives from a military base.

"Everyone good?" Jax asked the group.

"Steven. You didn't bring any water?" Ted asked.

"No. I didn't."

"You need to get a camelbak," Ted said, pointing to the pack of water on his back, holding the hose equipped with a mouthpiece attached to his tactical vest.

"Yeah. They're great. Here, take some water," Jax said, moving closer to me so I could reach the hose. It was cold and tasted good.

"Steven. That was the hard part. We're about a click out," Ted said.

"Sounds good," I told Ted, not even sure what a click translated to in distance.

The rest on top of the crest didn't help my back pain. Now cramping. Every step with my left foot a jolt of pain would shoot down my leg.

Billy was the first to find something, calling the group over to admire his treasures. Linked .50 caliber ammunition with tracer rounds. I didn't even know what it was at the time. Big bullets was how I later described it to G-Man and Mick. Linked with metal clips positioning each round side by side. Every fifth round had a colored tip. Billy stashed his treasures in his pack.

"Got something. Over here," Ted said.

I recognized this one. Hand grenades scattered over the desert floor. Round like baseballs.

"M69s. Let's take them. We can reuse the bodies and the fuse," Billy said.

I grabbed three of the grenades and shoved them in Jax's pack.

"These are live! Jackpot," Ted said. Grenades inside of a cardboard cylinder. Four in total. Ted snatched them up, placing them in his pack. We scoured the area for another hour, picking up spent casings, *brass*, the marines had left behind. Ted and Jax used the brass to reload their own ammunition.

The hike back to the rally point was tiring but rewarding. Our packs were heavy; not stuffed with meat from a long hunt but with ammunition, grenades and brass casings we'd just stolen from the United States Military.

Jax noticed me struggling to climb into the back of the truck. My back pain was severe.

"Are you okay, Steven?" he asked.

"Yeah. My back slammed up against the truck on the way out there. It's cramping but it will be okay," I said.

"Nice job, gentlemen! Nice job," Ted announced. "Listen. This is our little secret. We don't share or tell the others about our findings. Everyone clear?"

Everyone nodded.

It was a long night. Freezing. I never knew the desert could get so cold! Sleeping on the desert floor with a hurt back. Liz replaced with a rifle, a pistol, and two hand grenades – my share of the loot. My new bed companions. Not a fair trade, I thought. But my dad had always told me that life was not fair. My mind wandered to warmer and happier times. No longer focused on my performance as an undercover cop. Drew, my given name, seemed so distant. Drew was now Steven the militia man.

The next day kicked off with a qualification course that Jax and Ted were proposing as part of M.O.S.T. (Militia Officers Standardized Training). The course of fire required militia members to hit a target at 50, 100, 200, and 300 yards. No small feat with iron sights. I was the only one out of the Rainier group that hit the steel plates at 300 yards. Tom shot well out to 200 yards but struggled to hit the 300-yard marker. Kelly did better. I was proud of her in a strange way. By the end of the day, she was able to load and unload her rifle quickly. Hit the 100-yard target 7 out of 10 and 3 out of 10 on the 200-yard target.

For lunch beef stew was my choice. The baggie said beef stew, peanut butter and crackers, and cherry nut cake.

"Steven, do you like it?" Kelly asked me.

"No. It's terrible," I said, shaking my head trying to choke down another bite.

Jax and Ted heard me.

"Steven, you don't like it? Which one do you have?" Ted asked.

"The package said it's beef stew," I said.

"That one is delicious," Jack yelled.

"Are you serious?" I asked, looking at him.

"I love that one too, Jack!" Jax said.

"You guys are fucking crazy. It looks and tastes like dog food to me," I said.

They all burst into laughter.

"It looks like dog food to me too, Steven," Bob said.

"You won't shit for a week," Brian said.

After lunch the group broke into two patrol units and practiced the tactics and movements that Brian had covered on the whiteboard the day before. Our evening exercise was to conduct a two-mile patrol. A test. Jax and Ted had placed targets throughout the two-mile course. Each squad was to navigate the course and identify all of the targets along the way. Engage the targets with proper tactics and communications. Brian and Jax were the safety officers and judges. After two hours of practice the desert was taking its toll on the men and one woman who had now lost the flower in her hair. Unspoken, but by design I guess. Jax wanted a true test to see the militia's capabilities. Commitment. Weaknesses. Mindset.

"Team leaders. Break your squads and have them ready to set out in twenty minutes," Brian announced.

Tom was my squad's team leader and we were up second. He assigned me to rear guard. The most physically demanding position. The rear guard, the only rear facing member of the squad. Forced to walk backwards the majority of the time with a 180-degree field of vision responsibility. It sucked. I couldn't recall ever walking backwards for more than twenty feet. Certainly, walking backwards for two-miles carrying twenty pounds of gear, in desert boots on bad terrain was a first. Great calf workout.

"Incoming. Incoming. This is not a drill. Lock and load. Everyone get under the canopy. Grab your shit and get under the canopy now!" Jax began yelling.

A helicopter had been sighted and could now be heard off in the distance. The sound of chambering rifles and scrambling militia men and one woman without a flower in her hair rushing to cover under a desert camouflage canopy. Billy, Jack, and Ted, rifles at the ready, pointing at the incoming helicopter.

"Randy, take Steven and Billy with you to the high ground and cover the road. Switch to channel two on the radio. Move out now!" Jax yelled. "Engage on my command only! I say again. Engage on my command only!"

Randy, Billy and I headed out, running up the hillside to high ground, rifles in hand. Randy and Billy started to slow as they lost their air.

"Steven. Keep going. Get to high ground where you can see the road. Take the radio," Randy yelled, passing me a hand-held radio. I ran like Barry Sanders on a breakaway until I reached the top of the hill, collapsing onto my stomach. Winded. Trying to catch my breath. My prize, the road came into view. It was clear. No storm of government agents waiting to seize the militia's guns. Adrenalin dump. My heart was pounding. I couldn't catch my breath but my back pain had subsided.

"Stand down! Stand down! All clear," Jax's voice echoed over the radio.

Randy and Billy were still struggling to make it up the hill. I yelled down to them and let them know Jax's orders. Sitting on the hillside, rifles in hand, Billy nodded his head and raised his arm in acknowledgment before lying back on the hillside. I mirrored his behavior as the dirt latched to my sweat-filled head. Collecting my thoughts. The adrenalin still flowing. Reality set in of what had just occurred. Not knowing how I would have handled that situation if Jax had given the order to *engage*. The obvious conclusion was death. Mine, the occupants of the helicopter, and/or the personnel on the road if it was not clear. The deciding factor would have been my choice of action or inaction. *What the fuck am I doing?* I whispered out loud to myself.

"Steven. You on? Steven. Come up for base camp," I heard over the radio lying in the dirt next to me. *This guy is LAPD!* I thought to myself. *No way he's not.*

"Yeah. This is Steven," I replied.

"You good?" Brian asked me.

"Yeah. Do you want me to come back?" I asked.

"Yes. Go ahead and clear. Return to base," Brian said. Pissed. Hoping I was wrong about Brian. I started my walk back down the hill. G-Man and Mick in my head. *We need to identify Brian if he's LAPD.* Brian just made it to the top of my list. This guy better not be dirty. Dishonoring my badge. Teaching militia boys Ranger tactics.

Jax gave us an extra thirty minutes to get our shit together and calm the nerves. The group was fired up. Some were pissed at Jax, others applauding his leadership and strong posture against our make-believe enemy. There was a definite split amongst the group and the tension in the air was palpable. The first group, Squad No. 1, headed out to conduct the test, a two-mile live fire patrol through tough terrain with targets throughout the course. Squad No. 2, Tom's squad, my group, followed with a twenty-minute lag time. My body was beaten and tired so I knew the others had to feel the same way. The exhaustion was physical and mental, not a friend of live fire drills. Nor a friend of eight militia men and one woman with a new pink flower in her hair carrying loaded rifles and asked to complete a two-mile *test,* engaging targets along the way as a coordinated team. The test far outweighing their training, capabilities, and physical conditioning. The chances of an accidental discharge or shooting

266

someone were high in my mind. I have witnessed far better trained police officers under much better conditions accidently fire their weapons. This was a recipe for disaster. My goal was simple: don't get shot in the back.

Squad No. 2, a mix of the Rainier and Denali militia members, set out on patrol. Mike was point man, then there was Steve, Tom, Harold, Jason, Kevin, Johnny, Kelly, and myself. The pace was slow. Brian coached us as we moved across the desert floor. A volley of gunfire from Squad No. 1 echoed across the Valley, startling some of our group. Squad No. 1 had found their first target. The gun volley was short, with rapid fire. Our squad scanned the desert valley looking for our first target.

"Stagger your formation! Keep your distances. Don't get sucked in!" Brian yelled. "One fucking grenade will take this squad out. Spread out!" he yelled again. Thirty minutes into our patrol.

"Contact left! Contact left!" Mike yelled. The entire squad turned left, looking at a paper silhouette in a small ravine about fifty yards away. No one fired.

"Cease fire! Cease fire! Safeties on. Sling your weapons," Brian yelled. Patient. Not upset, but disappointed with our performance or lack of performance. Brian talked to the squad, reiterating the basics. Staggered formation when we're on patrol. Setting security when we stop for a break. Rules of engagement when a target is located. Don't hesitate. Engage immediately upon recognition. Field of fire responsibilities for each squad member. Who shoots and when. The pep talk or lecture set us back thirty minutes.

"Okay. Let's do this. We're back *live* but we need to pick the pace up. We have some time to make up," Brian told the group and off we went, missing our first target. Weaving up and down the desert floor, then taking a brief break in the ravine. Tom gave the signal for the squad to set security. The movement and reaction time was decent. Backs of militia men and one woman who had lost her pink flower again formed a protective barrier around Tom as he checked his map. Rifles at the ready.

"Everyone good? Let's move out," Tom told his squad.

It didn't take long. "Contact right! Contact right!" Mike said, followed by a volley of gunfire hitting a target up a hill about fifty yards away. A lull in the gunfire. *Beeeeeeeeeeeeeeeep!* A high pitch was ringing in my ears as I realized I'd forgotten to put my earplugs back in. Rookie move.

"Great job! Nice work!" Brian encouraged the squad.

"Move out!" Tom yelled. The adrenalin was helping the squad get through the physical aspects of the course. We reached the halfway point, making a turn to head back towards base camp. It didn't take long.

"Contact right! Contact right!" Mike yelled, followed by Steve, "Contact left! Contact left!" The gun fire was intense and so were the errors. Kelly's rifle malfunctioned. Mike forgot to reload his rifle and didn't realize it. Another pep talk/lecture and off we went. Thirty minutes later, the squad was dragging and losing focus. It was a hard hump, especially for those that were not in shape. Especially under those conditions.

Mike signaled Tom for a break. The squad automatically set security – an improvement.

"Steven. Mike is out. Can you take over point?" Brian asked.

"Sure," I replied.

"Harold. I need to you to stay with Mike. We'll call base camp and have someone pick you two up," Jason said.

Mike was cramping severely and couldn't continue, leaving just a few of us to complete the course. Kelly remained tough and determined to show the men she was an asset.

"You okay?" I asked her as she was taking a drink. She nodded, spilling water down her chin and splashing her face. The water creating streaks across her dirt-laden face, but she didn't seem to mind.

"Okay. Let's move out," Brian told the squad.

I was now positioned as the point. The front man. I quickened the pace as directed but the squad was falling behind. Tired and losing focus, their rifle muzzle discipline was gone. Rifles inadvertently pointing at each other's backs. Tom told me to slow my pace. Staying on course, keeping my head on a swivel. The sunlight beginning to call it a night. I crested a small hill. Multiple targets came into my view.

"Contact front! Contact front!" I yelled.

Bang… bang… bang… bang… There were six targets. The gun fire was close to me. I heard the whizz of a bullet go past my head during the melee. The squad peeled off, left, right, left, forming a firing line on my position. The gunfire continued. *Bang… bang… bang…* Some hits. Many misses.

"Stand down. Stand down. That's the end of the exercise, everyone. Great job. Everyone unload. Unload your weapons!" Brian told the squad.

The squad spoke about their disappointment with their performance on our short hump back to base camp. I didn't see it that way and I knew the Department wouldn't either.

That night, talk around the makeshift fire pit was jovial. Telling stories about shooting down helicopters, us charging the hill, Mike cramping, malfunctions, people tripping on patrol, missing targets, everyone's favorite MRE meals.

"Hey Jax. What's tomorrow's training look like again?" Billy asked.

"Tomorrow we start at 0800. Weapons cleaning. Then we'll start the qualification course. We'll probably have to break the qual course into three waves. After that, we'll debrief and then everyone can head out," Jax said.

"Hey. After qual, can we try out our new *toys*?" Billy asked.

"No," Jax said quickly.

"Not even..." Billy tried again, but Jax immediately cut him off.

"No!"

I didn't know what Billy meant by their *new toys*, but it was obvious it made Jax very uncomfortable in front of the group.

Rifle Qualification – Sunday Morning

The next morning, I replaced my MRE breakfast with two Tylenols. Not the breakfast of champions. But I wasn't worried about Wheaties calling me to pose for the next cereal box. Maybe *Time Magazine*. I wouldn't have been the first undercover person to make the magazine.

Jax put the Rainier militia in the first qualification relay and everyone was surprisingly nervous.

"Steven. Are you worried about this qualification?" Tom asked me.

"No. Are you?" I asked.

"I'm worried. Everyone has all of these fancy rifles with scopes and bipods. We don't have any of that," Tom said.

"That's exactly why you shouldn't be worried. The pressure is on them, not us. Besides, it's the shooter, not the rifle," I encouraged him.

"True. But I'm still nervous," he said.

"Who cares? Let's say you don't qualify. They can't kick you out of the militia. It's your group," I said and we both started to laugh.

The banter between the militia boys began to pick up as our start time neared. The instinctual competitiveness that's imperative for the survival of man. Not everyone gets a trophy in life. It was clear there was a *top shot* competition going on between militias. My intention this time was to win it. David, the crazy black militia man, and Bob from the Cypress group were the most vocal and I was tired of their lip.

"Steven. I'm going to take you down," David said, trying to get under my skin as usual. Little did he know he was just pissing me off and that makes me better.

"That didn't work out too well for you last time you tried. But good luck. I hope you do," I said. A bit of an aggressive approach but I couldn't help myself.

The others laughed. The top shooter in each relay would have a shoot-off at the end to decide who the overall top shooter was.

"Alright, boys. Let's get started. Rainier group, let's get on the line and make ready for live fire," Brian announced.

As we walked up to the line I told Tom., "You got this… don't sweat it."

Everyone shot really well. The improvement since Friday was tremendous. At the conclusion of all three relays there was only one member that did not qualify and they weren't from Rainier. Tom and Kelly had both qualified. They were so excited. To be transparent, Jax or Brian had apparently lowered the qualification standards from their initial instruction on Friday.

"Can I get Steven from Rainier (relay no. 1), Ralph from Denali (relay no. 2), and Bob from Cypress (relay no. 3)," Brian announced for the top shot competition. Everyone clapped after the announcement, which I thought was comical. Even more comical was that David hadn't made it to the final grouping.

"Slight change. To be fair, since Steven has a relic for a rifle with no glass, we're only shooting out to 100 yards," Brian announced. The group laughed in agreement about my relic of a gun. They were laughing, but I liked the rifle. It shot straight. It didn't malfunction. It just wasn't sexy and it looked the same when you woke up with it in the morning. I was very calm moving into the final round. The underdog. A label familiar to me. Motivating and meaning I had nothing to lose.

"Steven, you're up first. Make ready for live fire. Five shots center mass from a prone position," Brian announced.

ROUND NO. 1 – 50 Yards

Steven   Shot No. 1 – Hit. Scoring an eight.

Shot No. 2 – Hit. Scoring a ten.

Shot No. 3 – Hit. Scoring a nine.

Shot No. 4 – Hit. Scoring a nine.

Shot No. 5 – Hit. Scoring a nine.

I dropped five points. Not great. But not bad. My strategy. Don't beat myself. No misses. Make them beat me. Ralph was up next:

Ralph   Shot No. 1 – Hit. Scoring a ten.

Shot No. 2 – Hit. Scoring a ten.

Shot No. 3 – Hit. Scoring a nine.

Shot No. 4 – Hit. Scoring a ten.

Shot No. 5 – Hit. Scoring a nine.

Ralph shot well, dropping only two points. Bob was up next.

Bob   Shot No. 1 – Hit. Scoring a nine.

Shot No. 2 – Hit. Scoring a nine.

Shot No. 3 – Hit. Scoring a nine.

Shot No. 4 – Hit. Scoring a nine.

Shot No. 5 – Hit. Scoring a ten.

At the end of the first; Ralph was on 48, Bob 46, and I had 45 points. The last round was more difficult. Five shots at 100 yards. All headshots. The scoring changed here. A hit to the head was worth ten points. Anything less than that was a miss and you scored zero. I was up first again.

ROUND NO. 2 – 100 Yards (Head shots)

Steven   Shot No. 1 – Hit. Ten points.

Shot No. 2 – Hit. Ten points.

Shot No. 3 – Hit. Ten points.

Shot No. 4 – Hit. Ten points.

Shot No. 5 – Hit. Ten points.

"Ohhhhh." I heard cheers.

"Steven is clean, boys. Wow!" Brian said, adding pressure to Ralph and Bob.

"Ralph and Bob. You both have to shoot clean. One miss and you're out," Brian announced, tightening the noose. "Ralph, you're up."

Ralph   Shot No. 1 – Miss.

The boys yelled in disbelief. More cheers as the excitement built waiting for Bob to shoot. Ralph looked pissed. Everything was falling my way. Back slapping. Shit talking. The desert breeze coming alive.

Bob   Shot No. 1 – Hit. Ten points.
             Shot No. 2 – Hit. Ten points.
             Shot No. 3 – Hit. Ten points.
             Shot No. 4 – Miss!

Game over. I was the new top shot with my old relic of a rifle, Betty Sue. The crowd goes wild. Not really, but I always wanted to say that. The training was officially over. A short debrief and the break-down of camp were the only remaining items. The group made short order of those and everyone began to part ways within the hour. I was packing my car up and I didn't know what to do with the hand grenades. Did I leave them in my duffle bag? Were they safe? I didn't even know what kind of grenades they were. All seemed like logical questions to me.

"Hey Steven! Thanks for coming out, man. Great shooting," Jax said to me, placing his arm around me.

"Thanks, Jax. Lucky. They had all of the pressure," I said.

"It was fun to watch them squirm," Jax said.

I laughed in agreement.

"Hey. I have a shipment of twelve lowers coming in soon. Would you be interested in one?" Jax said.

"Lowers? What's that?" I asked and he laughed at my ignorance.

"AR-15 rifle lowers. They're the most important part of the rifle because that's where the serial number is. You technically have to register the lower. That's how the government tracks your guns. We don't do that. I have a connection that gets me unregistered lowers. We need to get you one and I'll build you a rifle," he said.

"I'd love to but my cash is tight right now. How much do I need?" I asked.

"Just buy the lower right now. They're $250," Jax said.

"That's not bad. I could probably do that. When do you need it by?" I asked.

"Ted and I are supposed to go pick them up in Vegas next month. But keep that on the down low," Jax said.

"I won't. Okay. If I have until next month I can do it. Put me down for one," I said.

"Just one? Try and get two if you can," he said.

"Will do," I said. "Hey. Are these grenades safe in my bag?"

"Yeah. They're fine. Don't worry about them. We're going to set up some training on them later so just hold on to them until then."

"Okay. Will do," I said. We shook hands and went to say our goodbyes to the remaining members before heading out. One last piece of business was on my mind. Brian's license plate. *1 All Be Nice, 045. Got it. In-N-Out Burger here I come.*

The drive was decompressing. Does it get any better than a drive with perfectly salted fries, an ice-cold soda with extra ice, George Strait playing, and a couple of hand grenades in the trunk? The burger didn't have a chance. I was starving.

Mick had the on call but I wanted to wait until I got closer to the city before I stopped to call him. Keeping my speed down – I didn't think I would be able to explain hand grenades in my trunk. After I hit the county line: bathroom break, gas, and a perfect line of pay phones.

"What's up, sweetheart? Did you miss me?" I answered the pay phone when it rang.

"I did, baby! Are you back?" Mick asked. He was in a good mood. He generally was unless he was in go mode.

"Not yet. I'm probably thirty minutes out. But I had to pee," I said.

"How did it go?" he asked.

"Good. I have a couple of hand grenades in my trunk right now," I said.

"Shut up," he said, laughing.

"I do," I said.

"You have hand grenades in the back of your car right now?" Mick said, transitioning from jovial to questioning.

"Yup. We stole them from the military base," I said, realizing how bad that seemed when I said it.

"You guys stole grenades from a military base?" Mick repeated in disbelief.

"Yeah. And they're in my trunk," I said.

"What kind of grenades are they?"

276

"No idea. The kind that go boom?" I said, but Mick wasn't laughing.

"You're serious, aren't you?" he said again in disbelief. "Fuck me. Hey, hold tight. Let me call G-Man and I'll call you right back."

The phone rang again about ten minutes later. It was G-Man.

"Hey, Steven. Mick told me the news. Where are you at?" he asked me. Calm as usual.

"I'm in Monterey Park at a Shell station," I said.

"Hey, listen. We're going to have to call out the bomb squad to take those grenades. Can you find a place where we can meet that's secluded? Maybe a school or church parking lot?" he asked.

"Seriously? I'm going to need these grenades. Bomb squad can't take them. How is that going to work?" I asked.

"Not sure. But we'll figure it out. Don't worry. Find us a location and Mick and I will meet you there," he said.

Forty-five minutes later he and Mick rolled into the back of a school parking lot where I was waiting.

"Hey, jump in my car," G-Man said through his window.

"Do you want to see them?" I asked.

"No, not yet, but I can't have you sitting in your car with a couple of hand grenades when the bomb squad rolls out. They'll kill me," G-Man said.

I'd forgotten. Back to reality. Liabilities. Protocols. Procedures. Policies.

"I told them I can't have this as a big production with lights and sirens, perimeters, command posts, news media. I hope they don't screw us. The Lieutenant is on his way too, FYI," G-Man said.

"The Lieutenant is coming out here? What for? Am I in trouble?" I asked.

Mick, sitting shotgun, chimed in, "You're stupid if you don't think the Lieutenant is going to roll out when one of his *birds* stole some hand grenades from a military base. Oh yeah, and is cruising around the city like they're a couple of baseballs in his trunk."

G-Man jumped on board with the smack talking, "Oh yeah, and you forgot about the part that the militia is now armed with grenades."

Mick and G-Man started laughing at my expense.

"Okay. Okay. Well, when you put it that way I get it. But for the record I didn't steal those grenades," I said, laughing.

"How does that even happen? For tonight's entertainment let's go steal some grenades on a military base?" Mick was poking fun but also wanted to know the story.

"Pretty much. And guess what. I think the guy that did most of the training is an LAPD guy," I said.

"What do you mean an LAPD guy?" G-Man and Mick both asked.

"His first name is Brian. I don't know his last name but I think he's LAPD. I got his plate," I said.

The tone turned even more serious.

"Why do you think that?" Mick asked.

"The commands he was giving during the training. Certain terms. The phrases. He has to be LAPD," I said.

"You're telling me that there was an active LAPD guy there training the militia in police tactics?" G-Man asked.

"Not really police tactics. He taught us Army Ranger tactics and LAPD firearms training. But I could be wrong. He might not be," I said.

278

"There was a dude out there teaching the militia Army Ranger tactics!?" Mick asked in disbelief.

"Yeah," I said.

"Oh, shit! What else did you guys do?"

"Hey. Let's not get ahead of ourselves. Let's get past these grenades and either confirm or eliminate Brian as one of ours," said G-Man. "Mick. Go call in his plate, but not over the radio though."

Mick went to his car. Minutes later, a blue unmarked suburban and two vehicles arrived, pulling into the dimly lit school parking lot. G-Man flashed his lights twice, signaling our location to the vehicles. My car with the hand grenades was parked by itself on the other side of the parking lot as a safety protocol. As the vehicles approached our car, Mick rolled down his window and gave a quick nod to G-Man and myself.

"Damn it!" G-Man said under his breath. "Hey, stay in the car. I don't want the bomb guys to see you."

It seemed like such a production to me. It was a Sunday. God's day. Family day. Called away from their families: Mick, G-Man, bomb guy no. 1, bomb guy no. 2, bomb supervisor, and the Lieutenant of ATD. Mick's nod confirmed I'd been right about Brian. He was an LAPD officer. I was going to be there all night, I thought.

Forty-five minutes later the bomb crew had cleared the scene, leaving the Lieutenant talking to G-Man and Mick for what seemed like forever. I was tired and starting to doze off in the car. The verdict: two live hand grenades; live 50-caliber ball ammunition with three live tracer rounds. I was expecting the Lieutenant to speak with me or ask me questions but they never came. He left, back off to his family, I assumed.

"Did he take my grenades?" I asked the boys when they got back in the car.

"Yup. Your grenades went bye-bye," Mick said.

"Don't worry. We'll figure it out," G-Man said.

"Wait. Wait. It's clear, right? Everyone's gone. Let's debrief at my car," Mick said. "I stopped and bought you a gift on my way here."

He reached into his back seat and pulled out a six pack of beer.

"A celebratory toast!" he said, handing myself and his supervisor, G-Man, a beer.

"Cheers, boys! Nice fucking work, Steven!" G-Man said, raising his beer.

Just what the doctor ordered for me. Cold. It tasted so good. Three cops enjoying a cold one in a school parking lot. Celebrating me stealing a couple of hand grenades from a military base with some militia boys, one of whom was an LAPD officer and former Army Ranger, all armed to the teeth running around the city bent on overturning the government. Seemed like a good reason to celebrate.

Accepting the Darkness

The 29 Palms training united, divided, and polarized the Southern California militia movement. The Western Marksmen Association militia proved that they had the ability to train up the untrained in guerilla warfare tactics, ready for a fight against their own government. Talk spread quickly. Lots of talk. Too much talk, some which hit the FBI chatter collection boxes, raising more red flags. Only reaching half mast, but nevertheless raised. The training event was monumental within the movement and law enforcement agencies were taking notice. Southern California militia men and one woman who generally had a flower in her hair also had to decide if they wanted to be operators or mouthpieces. Law enforcement agencies had to decide how to deal with this growing movement. Were militias exercising their constitutional freedoms including free speech and the right to bear arms or were they a front for criminal organizations?

Over the next few months, the Western Marksmen Association distinguished themselves as the most advanced or dangerous militia group depending on which hat you were wearing. Some members in attendance on that monumental day never went back, only to be replaced with new faces over the coming months. There didn't seem to be a shortage of new recruits angry at our government eagerly wanting to join the ranks. With every new member and new faction my status within the movement was elevated. The movement caught fire, becoming more organized, training more often in advanced techniques. The basic training was offered to the masses but only the privy, the chosen few, operators, were invited to the advanced stuff.

The communication between groups moved to PGP (Pretty Good Privacy), a government-developed encrypted communication platform released to the public by what was referred to as a sympathizer, now being widely used within the militia movement. Weapons. It goes without saying there were always guns when you mention the word militia, second amendment enthusiasts, but it grew beyond that. The militias were stockpiling weapons, equipment and ammunition. Caching weapons in secret locations, friends' backyards, the national forest, and in one case a secret underground bunker out in the Valley. Jax's group had become better equipped and better trained than most local law enforcement SWAT teams and he was supplying and building illegal unregistered AR-15 rifles to specific militia members. He built me a CAR-15 with a collapsible stock and flash suppressor, along with thirteen thirty-round magazines, a tactical vest and a three-point rifle sling.

Investigation

LAPD and the Anti-Terrorist Division (ATD) were in a pickle. My involvement within the militia movement became too deep. I must have missed the *too deep* class in my training, which some have argued to be one of the deepest in the history of the program. Nevertheless, it was uncharted territory that brought problems for the Department and the investigation. My involvement in criminal activity and knowledge of the same was extensive. Illegal weapons, explosives, numerous thefts from a military base, fraud with fake liens, personal knowledge of ongoing threats to public officials including a judge, just to mention a few. That's the pickle? All information that only the chosen few were privy to, including me. If the Department acted on the information and began making arrests I'd be exposed and so would the program. Also, the opinion at the time was that the militias would go underground, validating their position against the government and causing further angst. The LAPD investigation would flip from proactive to reactive, no longer gathering intelligence and having the upper hand if there was a greater plan such as an Oklahoma City bombing.

The Department discussions I was not present or directly privy to, but I know they were fierce. JT's crew, the training unit, were trying at all costs not to expose the program's existence with arrests. Their livelihoods. Their self-proclaimed legacy. Some were demanding that the Chief give the order to pull me out of the program. I was too deep. I wasn't safe. On the investigative side, G-Man and Mick were arguing that it wasn't an option. The program's life was second to mine and the investigation. The Department's primary duty was to preserve life, not to preserve the program. My continued existence under the sheets would undoubtedly save lives. The discontent within the ATD was palpable even from under the sheets.

Mindset

As I was approaching my two-year mark the investigation continued to steamroll; Drew's life was distant. The more time I clocked under the sheets, the further I separated myself from him. Dad, Mom, Sis, friends, it didn't matter. Liz. Liz who? A distant blanket of safety I wanted, demanded and maybe secretly desired. People move on. Out of sight, out of mind is true. Saying that I'd begun to like my new militia life was a stretch, but I certainly didn't mind it. Living on the edge. The criminal activity. The firearms training. The tactical training, assaulting targets in the desert, forest, or the city. The adrenaline rushes were euphoric. All of it addicting. A natural drug, but make no mistake, it was a drug. A life without a moral compass, or at least a license to disable it when convenient. Applauded and praised for insouciant behavior. My conscience, in the tenth round of a prize fight, towel in hand.

Socially comfortable. My time was split between Steven's best friend, Lupe, and Jax from the Western Marksmen Association. Yup, that's right. Lupe and Jax. Two different people from different worlds. I'm not sure if I could or should use the term *friend* in either case. Depends on your definition and if you're asking me or them. Lupe and I would watch a movie, grab a drink, play board games, grab dinner or just talk. Jax and I would build rifles, reload ammunition, talk tactics, test optics, grab a bite to eat or just hang out. Friends? You decide.

Joint Rainier and Denali Park Militia Meeting

The following week G-Man, Mick and I briefed before the meeting at a Denny's in the Valley.

"Hey boss. How are you? Is Mick coming?" I asked.

"Yeah," G-Man said. "He's running late. You should know that by now. I ordered your Yankee pot roast and soda for you. We're going to be tight on time so we're not waiting for him."

"Great. Thanks, boss," I said, taking a sip of my soda.

"So how are you doing?" G-Man asked.

"I'm good, thanks. How's your daughter doing in softball?" I asked.

"She's throwing really well. The other night she pitched a one hitter. I hated to miss that one but I was proud of her," G-Man said.

"I'm sorry, boss," I said, realizing that he'd missed his daughter's game because he was covering me at a meeting. Knowing he and Mick were missing more and more of their family commitments for me and this investigation. The sacrifice expanding to their wives and children for an unknown cause or mission their loved ones were not privy to know anything about. A situation that couldn't be described or documented with the eloquent words of a writer. It was simply shitty.

"No. I didn't mean it like that or to make you feel bad. It's the job," he said, taking a drink of his Diet Coke.

I didn't answer, just gave him a nod of acknowledgement. A non-verbal thank you.

"Thank you," G-man said.

"Thank you… Really. I mean it. Thank you," I said, looking him in the eye with another nod of my head.

G-Man accepted my thanks with a nod of his own. I noticed him swallow with a slight exhale. A rare non-verbal sign, involuntary, it showed how the magnitude and gravity of this investigation was weighing on him and his family.

Mick showed up shortly after my dinner arrived but I'd lost my appetite. My conscience was filling in for the hunger pains, wondering if this investigation was worth it.

"Let's go, boys. Finish up. We have work to do," G-man said, back in go mode.

"Hey boss. I'm not done?" Mick said, throwing his hands up in the air and looking at his plate of food.

"You should have shown up on time then. Let's go," G-Man said, getting up from the table.

"Is he serious? I'm starving," Mick said, still in disbelief, but I knew G-Man was serious. It was a big night for our team. I heard Mick say, "For fuck's sake," still talking to himself as he got up from the table, grabbing his biscuit and mine. It made me chuckle and lightened my mood. I was a bit nervous for the first time in a while.

We met out in the rear parking lot of the Denny's at G-Man's car. Mick with a mouth full of bread, me laughing at him as I removed my shirt. G-Man testing the wire and receiver equipment.

"Test, test, test. It sounds good," G-Man said, showing me the wire and explaining how it worked. Old technology back then, similar to this one. Not exactly stealth.

 The wire itself was attached to a shoulder rig not shown here. Similar to a bra worn backwards, not that I have ever worn a bra, but you get my point. Slip your left and right arm through the straps and the battery pack/transmitter (large black box) was tucked away in a pocket under my left armpit. The antenna was fed through the shoulder strap securing it. The brown cord was the mic fed through the other side of the shoulder strap resting in the middle of my chest. A piece of tape secured it to my skin. The receiver, housed in a black briefcase, recorded everything onto a cassette tape. However, it was a one-way street. They could hear me, but that was the extent of the communication.

"How does that feel? Put your shirt on and let me see what it looks like," G-Man said.

I did what he said with blind trust, relying on his expertise.

"I want you to have at least two layers of clothing on. Would that look suspect for an inside meeting?" he asked.

"No. Not at all. I'll wear my hoodie," I said matter-of-factly.

G-Man's nerves and Mick's hunger pains were evident as I threw on my hoodie.

"I like that. Turn around for me. That looks good. Walk over there and talk," G-Man asked.

"Jingle bells, jingle bells, jingle all the way. Oh, what fun it is to ride in a one horse…" I began to sing as I walked away.

"Okay, okay. Please stop! We're good," Mick yelled, shaking his head.

"It sounds great. Listen to me. I need a word or a phrase from you. If you get in trouble just say it twice. You hear me? Say it twice and we're coming in." G-Man was calm but amped, in protective mode now.

"*Blue Moon*. I'll say *Blue Moon*," I said without hesitation.

"What the fuck is blue moon?" Mick said, laughing, genuinely perplexed.

"*Blue Moon* it is. Do you have any questions?" G-Man said, wanting to get the party started.

"No sir. I'm good," I said.

"Listen. We're going to have a team out there tonight sitting on the house. So don't worry, we'll have you covered. Just say the phrase and in the troops will come."

"Boss, boss," I interrupted him. "I got this." I knew he was worried and he needed to hear it in my voice.

He nodded with a slight tilt of his head and shook my hand before grabbing his police radio. "Thirty David. The package is rolling. Report to your posts."

Mick was strapping on his vest and loading his shotgun near his car. We locked eyes and I gave him a nod.

"Hey! Come here, baby. Let's do this. Fuck these guys," Mick said as we high fived each other with a smile. He was over his hunger pains and in hunt mode. Eyes locked and lips pursed, shotgun at the ready, his weapon of choice, looking to kill anything that fucked with me.

The meeting was at Jason's place. There was nothing special about tonight's meeting other than that I was wearing a wire for the first time. The new normal moving forward. As I turned onto Jason's street, there was a vehicle slowing, illuminating its brake lights directly in front of his house. I knew it had to be part of G-Man's surveillance team. *Such a bone head move*, I thought as my confidence in his team shrank.

Standing room only again. Militia members shoulder to shoulder. *He needs a larger living room*, I thought. The agenda was long. Gary, the commander from the San Fernando militia, was in attendance with some *vital* news for the group. After the Pledge of Allegiance and opening prayer.

Jason opened the meeting. "Thank you everyone for attending. We have a full agenda tonight so let's get started." He passed out a typed agenda. First on the list was a new special order from the LAPD. "Real quick. This is from my law enforcement sources within the LAPD. The

289

LAPD issued a special order to all of its troops outlining how to use cayenne pepper pills to stop bleeding in the field. I propose that everyone throws in $10 and we make a bulk purchase. All in favor raise your hand."

The group raised their hands in favor.

"Steven, what's your vote?"

I must have been daydreaming or still processing what I'd just heard. Crazy. Not even close to logical. "Yeah, I'm in," I said.

"Great. Moving on. Here are a few updates from old business items. More unmarked black helicopters have been spotted over militia members' houses and in one instance following a member at a high altitude to his residence. The helicopters were counter-surveilled by other members and tracked to LAPD's air support division where they landed. I have my LAPD sources checking on that and I'll provide an update next meeting. The other items we'll table just for membership.

"The next topic I want to open up to the floor. Some members have voiced concerns about Jax and his group and do not want our group to associate with them anymore or attend their trainings," he announced.

"Who said that?" asked Ralph.

"They came to me in confidence so I am not at liberty to say," Jason said.

"If you said it, speak up, motherfucker!" Ralph said, looking around the room.

"Ralph. We're not doing that. I just want to have a general discussion about it and what's best for our group," Jason said.

The tension in the air thickened. I sensed that David, the crazy black militia man, was off again tonight. Maybe he didn't take his meds or the crazy squirrel in his head was on crack. He had his pistol in his waistband tonight.

"May I ask what issue they have with Jax's group is? Is there information out there that maybe we don't know about that makes them feel that way?" Tom asked Jason.

"Good point, Tom. The issue is that Jax's group is drawing a lot of attention to itself with all of the advanced training it's conducting. That's making some people feel uncomfortable. They believe it's too high profile and there is too much co-mingling of units. They had concerns about how much attention the training might be drawing to our group."

"That's stupid. We're already hot! Your trashes were already searched were they not and we have black helicopters following us? There are probably surveillance units out there right now watching us?" Ralph said; little did he know that he was right and everything was being recorded.

"Understood. Good point, Ralph," Jason said.

David's thousand-mile stare was coming into focus. I sensed he was going to lose it so I repositioned myself near the front door, looking for cover.

"Should Jax's group not train us then? Maybe we're the ones bringing heat on his group? As soon as there's a little heat we're going to shut down? What the fuck," Ralph said, still pissed.

"I think one of you motherfuckers is a snitch. And all of this stuff is bullshit!" David suddenly yelled to the group, locking eyes with a new guy in attendance, someone I didn't know. David didn't mess with me anymore after the knife incident. We'd grown to have a mutual understanding and

291

he'd actually sold me an illegal assault rifle a few months back. The sale caught on video by my boys G-Man and Mick.

I knew this was David's MO: prey on the new guy. But there wasn't a doubt in my mind that he wouldn't shoot me if this went to guns. The new guy had frozen. He might have even diddled in his pants, but I wasn't fighting his battle tonight. I wasn't in the mood. My objective was simple: don't get dead.

"David. Shut up. Stand down. I'm not saying that, Ralph. I just want to make sure that everyone is on the same page and good with the group as a whole participating in Jax's training," Jason said, steering the conversation back to his question.

David looked amped. Crazy as a sprayed cockroach. His gun hand twitching. His breathing elevated.

"I say we vote now! Why are we waiting until next week if it's that important?" Ralph said.

"I'm with Ralph. I'm tired of these fucking pussies," David said in his crazy-as-a-runover-cat voice. "All you guys just want to sit around and talk about black helicopters, the New World Order, chips, Mexicans but you never do shit. We need to keep training and take it to these motherfuckers. Anyone not down for the cause, you can get the fuck out now is my vote."

"David. Just relax, man. Relax," Ralph said. But the members in the know knew that he was a ticking time bomb tonight.

"David. I appreciate and love your passion, but we're not voting tonight," Jason reiterated.

"Fuck this, man. I'm out of here," David said, grabbing the gun out of his front waistband. Right hand this time. Muzzle pointed down, his finger along the frame. Good technique, I thought, as he walked in my direction towards the front door.

"David! Put the gun away, man. Just relax," Jason said in a calm voice, stepping in his path, others looking for cover. I stood my ground, wondering if G-Man and Mick had heard that. I imagined Mick was low crawling towards the front door with his shotgun in hand, ready to come in blazing, G-Man right behind him. It made me laugh inside. Some might even say that I'm the one that's crazy, but I wasn't scared. I was entertained.

David, standing in the middle of the room and looking from side to side, was still holding his gun and not listening to Jason. The safety was off and his finger was along the trigger. It was as if he hadn't even heard Jason. Nothing upstairs was registering and everyone was staring at him, hoping he wouldn't snap.

I broke the silence. "When did you switch to a Berretta?" I asked him.

He looked down at his gun.

"I think that's the new model," I said. "Mine is old. I want to check that out later if that's cool?"

"Yeah, I'll show you. I like it," David said, putting away his gun and walking back to his spot on the couch. The new guy, realizing the insanity, got up. "Hey, Jason. I have to go. Thanks for inviting me." Out the door he went and I never saw him again. I felt bad for the guy, but it was probably a good thing for him.

"Hey. Let's cut this meeting short tonight. Emotions are too high and I'll see everyone next week," Jason said reluctantly and surprisingly no one argued with his decision. Not even David.

I left the meeting with everyone else, not getting the chance to check out David's new gun like he'd promised I could. My focus had switched to getting out of this house, hoping that G-Man's surveillance team staged outside was on their game and didn't get burned.

Debrief

G-Man, Mick and I met back at the Denny's parking lot but we didn't eat this time. After the all-clear sign, I walked over to them with a slight grin on my face.

"You're right! That dude is 5150. That was some crazy shit! I was like, 'Let's go, motherfucker. Let's get some!' And G-Man was just, 'Calm down. He's got it handled,'" Mick said, all fired up and laughing out loud.

"Nice work, man. Way not to panic," G-Man acknowledged my performance – or lack of performance.

"You're good, man. The way you talk to those crazy fuckers. I don't know how you do it," Mick said, still fired up as I removed my shirt to take the anchor of a wire off my chest. Free again.

"I think we need to take David down. He's a problem. How much heat would it put on you if we arrested him?" G-man asked.

"As long as you don't arrest him for the illegal assault weapon I bought off him, I'm clear," I said.

"How will the militia react if we take him down?" G-Man asked.

"Oh, they'll flip, but I don't think they would be surprised. They all know he's crazy. Some might even be relieved if he got arrested," I said.

"So you're good with it?" G-Man asked again.

"Heck yeah! I can't stand that guy, but what are you going to arrest him on?"

"Not sure. But we'll find something," G-Man said.

"I'm good with it, but be careful. As you heard. He's crazy. He just might go to guns," I said with a serious tone.

"*I'll bet he's huckleberry*," Mick chimed in.

G-Man ignored him. "Okay. I'll let you know what the decision is when I know it. Go get some sleep. Nice work tonight, boys," G-Man said, taking off his bullet proof vest.

"You boys up for a beer?" Mick asked.

"Sure," I said.

"I can't tonight, but you boys behave yourself. I won't be there to babysit you two," G-Man said, preoccupied already with trying to figure out a tactical plan to arrest David.

Mick and I went off to the bar to grab a cold one and tell more lies.

Mom

Not the militia of Montana type. My mother. It had been a while since we'd spoken and Mick was on me to make sure I called her. She was my backbone of support. My compass back to my core. Relentless in her efforts to stay connected with me even though she knew nothing and I mean nothing about my current life. Not my name, address, phone number, assignment. Nothing. I could avoid, dodge, turn a blind eye to everything except my mother. It wasn't an option. She refused to allow it and everyone knew it. No one wanted the wrath of a MacGregor mother when it came to her children and I knew Mick was right. I was overdue in calling her.

"Oh. Hi, baby, how are you! I knew it was you!" she said excitedly.

"I'm good, Ma. Sorry it's been a while," I said, hoping the upfront apology would save me from the tongue lashing I deservedly had coming.

"Yes, I know it's been too long. I was getting ready to call that guy Mick if I didn't hear from you today," she said in a tone.

"Yeah. I figured. Sorry," I apologized again.

"I've done it before and I'll do it again baby. You know I will."

"Yes. Everyone knows, Ma," I said, shaking my head.

"That guy Mick, your handler, called me a few days ago and I got so scared! I thought something had happened to you and I started crying. I felt so dumb because he was just checking on me. He felt so bad for scaring me," my mother went on. She'd always been a talker.

"Have you talked to your sister or your dad lately?" she asked.

"Yeah, I talked to them both a couple of weeks ago and Cindy wrote me. It was good to speak to them both."

"Your sister said that your dad got remarried! Did you know that? Did you go?" she asked.

"Oh wow. No. He didn't mention it. I guess I didn't get the invite but I couldn't have made it anyway. Great. I hope he's happy," I said, surprised by the news. "What's up with Cindy? Anything new with her?" I asked.

"Yeah, your sister got promoted and started a new job. I think she likes it but I wish she had more time to herself. She's always working and doesn't have any fun, you know. Life is too short and you should have some fun too," my mom rambled, with one foot on her soapbox.

"Good for her. I miss you guys. Tell her hi for me next time you speak with her," I said.

"Oh, I'll call her right after I hang up the phone with you. We made a pact that when one of us hears from you we call each other immediately."

"You guys are too much," I said with a smile.

"So how are you? You sound better to me this time. Are you good?" she asked.

"I am good, Mom. So how is grandma doing?"

"Don't change the subject on me. Do you remember your promise to me, son?"

"Yes, ma'am. I do."

"Okay. Are you keeping your promise?"

"Yes, ma'am. I am. I promise, and no, I have not been to church recently," I said, knowing her routine line of questioning.

"Drew MacGregor. You need to go to church," she said as her voice cracked with emotion.

"Yes, ma'am. It's tough, Ma," I tried to say but she stopped me mid-sentence.

"Now, MacGregor, I don't want to hear your excuses. Please. Do it for your mother," she pleaded.

"I will, Ma. I promise," I said, knowing that if I promised she'd know it would happen.

Samantha

Ring, ring, ring... A rare telephone call at my apartment.

"Hello?" I said.

"Hey. It's Sam. Don't worry, I'm calling you from a pay phone. You don't have any meetings tonight right?"

"No. Not tonight," I replied.

"I'm bored. Let's go grab a drink and catch up?"

"Ahh." I hesitated. Quarterly training must be around the corner or she must be plotting, I thought. A familiar pattern of Samantha's. Complex. Flirtatious. Attractive. Trailing a seductive web. Personal and business motives never transparent. Always walking the line with a smile but never crossing it. I was curious to know if her contact with me was of her own volition or directed by JT and the training unit. Was her flirtatious nature genuine or a means to an end? Friend or foe? Good or bad? Which side of the line would she fall when pushed? And a push was inevitable.

"Come on. Let's go. You name the place," she said.

I agreed, settling on a Mexican place about twenty minutes away. When I arrived we went through our normal op sec protocols, giving each other the all-clear sign.

"Look at you. I like the rugged mountain man look," she said, petting my beard, which had grown thick.

"Thanks. I'm not a fan but it's part of the job, you know. It hides my baby face," I said.

"Part of your job? What do you do for a living, sir?" Sam joked. Role playing. Her comfort zone as we walked inside.

"I can tell you. But then I would have to kill you," I said, repeating one of my favorite movie lines.

"Oh wow. Your job is top secret? Don't worry about it. You can tell me. I have a secret clearance," she whispered in my ear.

"Great! You can read about it then," I said, whispering back into her ear, continuing with the *Top Gun* theme.

"It's good to see you," Sam said, giving me a once over.

"You too! It's been a while," I said, as we hugged. Longer than a greeting. Her body was harder than I remembered, but it had been awhile since I'd felt her touch.

"You changed perfumes. It's nice. I like it," I said.

"Wow. You're good," Samantha said as we walked towards a corner table located in the bar area. Chips and salsa. Cadillac margaritas on the rocks with salt. A shared plate of chicken fajitas with flour tortillas and guacamole. The conversation light. Never personal or meaningful.

"You've changed," she said, finishing her first margarita.

"How so? Would you like another drink?"

"Yeah. I'll take another drink and let's do a shot. All grown up, I guess. You just seem different to me," she said.

"Time under the sheets makes you grow up, I guess," I said, ordering two more margaritas and a couple of shots.

"It does. How long have you been under now?" Sam asked.

"Two years, I believe," I said, nodding my head in amazement.

"It's been two years already?" Sam said.

"Yup. I can't believe it," I said. Not realizing it until I said it out loud. "What about you? How have you been?" I asked.

"I've been good. Thank you for asking. The boys drive me nuts. But I'm good. They would have a shit-fit if they knew I was here right now," she said.

"Really? I thought they sent you," I said.

"What? You think the boys sent me to see you?" Sam put down her drink. Bothered by my statement.

"I do. You always seem to pop up just before quarterly training," I said.

"Fuck you! That's bullshit, Steven, and you know it," she said. Pissed.

"Oh wow. That's a little aggressive," I said.

"Take it back. Take it back right now," she said, leaning forward and grabbing my hand.

"Not sure that I can. Someday, Sam, we can be real with each other. But today, I don't think is the day, so let's just go back to playing the game," I said.

"Oh really? Let's make it the day then. Let's be real. Three questions each," Sam said, holding up her shot glass and looking at mine still on the table.

"Okay. I'll play. Cheers. Ladies first. Question number one," I said. Toasting each other with the shots.

Samantha paused. "Back in training," she said. "The girl that got you choked out. Did you know that she was a UC?"

"I figured that was going to be a question... It's generally the girl that gets me into trouble. Yeah, I knew," I said.

"Then why would you go into the house?"

"That's number two," I said.

"No. You can't count that! That's not fair," Samantha said, laughing.

"Life's not fair. I can and I did count that one," I said.

Samantha just shook her head.

"I went into the house because I was curious to see what you devious people had in store for me. I didn't know I was going to get choked out. Crazy," I said.

"Neither did I! That was crazy. Nobody knew," Sam said.

"You didn't know they were going to choke me out?"

"That's question number one! And no, I didn't. Nobody did. That was all Jack. JT was pissed," Sam revealed.

"Really? What a dick. Him and I are going to dance one day," I said.

"I know, right? No one could believe it. It was not part of the plan. He does not like you!" Sam said, laughing as she finished her second margarita.

"Really? I didn't notice. Does he like anyone?" I asked with a sarcastic tone.

"That's question number two. That's question number two! And no, I don't even think he likes his own mother," Sam said, laughing, proud of herself.

"Well. Looks like the score is tied and it's the bottom of the ninth. One question left each. You're up," I said.

Sam paused for a long time contemplating her last question, taking a few drinks of her fresh margarita. Then she leaned across the table, motioning with her finger for me to lean forward. She whispered in my ear, "Do you want to fuck me?"

Shocked, but not shocked by her directness, I smiled and leaned back in my seat contemplating before I answered. Samantha growing restless.

"Was that an offer?" I asked.

"That's a tactic, not an answer, Mac," she said, breaking op sec protocol, her upper torso now lying across the table, leaning on her elbow. Her head braced by the palm of her hand. Hair freshly washed. Curled. Flowing down onto the table. Black blouse falling forward, exposing my favorite part of her body, her breasts. A grain of salt stuck to her full lips. I locked eyes with her and began to move towards her. An intimate game of chicken. She didn't move… I felt her breath on my face. Our lips dangerously close. She didn't move… I kissed her lips once, tasting the salt. Soft and full. Tequila. She remained still… I kissed her lips again. Eyes still locked. She didn't move…

"That's my answer," I said, sitting back in my seat.

"I liked your answer," Sam said, still not moving. "What's your last question?" she said, smiling with her eyes.

"I'm going to save my last question. I need to go," I said, motioning to the waiter for our check.

"Really? You're going to leave me? We were just making progress, I thought," Sam said, prompting a chuckle from me. She slid her hand out on the table. Palm up. An invitation. A gesture. Not sure. I accepted. Soft hands. Well-manicured. "Come here," she said, pulling my hand towards her. Lifting her head up. She kissed me passionately across the table. "Are you sure you have to go?" she whispered.

I kissed her back. "I'm sure. But this was nice. Thanks for calling," I said, getting up from the table. A lean-in kiss goodbye on her cheek. A mutual metro nod goodbye and I didn't look back, knowing I would change my mind if I did. A self-made promise intact. No distractions. Besides, tomorrow was a work day…

An otherwise normal day working in retail. The store was filled mostly with women; mothers or wives killing time, grabbing a few necessities, browsing the aisles, generally spending too much money on items flashing a sale price that was too great to pass up. Plotting how to hide the items from the man in their life or rehearsing the speech that most women give, focusing on how much money they'd *saved* negating how much they may have spent. An occasional man, most likely coming in to grab something he had forgotten or been asked to pick up.

"Call 911. Call 911," I heard Nester call out to Salvador, who was working the cash register next to me. "Code blue, code blue to Toys." A panicked voice sounded across the store intercom. A medical emergency. A woman was crying hysterically, saying something in Spanish that I couldn't understand. Clinching a small infant to her chest. A tight hug, extending her arms outward, hoping her child would breathe. The infant wasn't old enough to speak or walk; her eyes said everything. She knew she was in trouble. Her lips were turning blue as the life was leaving her body. The mother turning from side to side, slapping the infant on her back. The only words I understood from the mother's screaming were "No" and "Nina". Flashback: Spanish would have been a better choice in high school. Latin, a dead language, wasn't helping me here.

The baby's condition was declining rapidly. Nothing was working. Surveying the growing audience, I knew I was the baby's best option.

"Give her to me! Give her to me!" I yelled, stepping forward. My arms extended, nodding my head up and down to the panicked mother.

She was reluctant. "Nester. Tell her in Spanish to give me the baby! Tell her!" I said. Nester, speaking Spanish, took the distressed baby from the mother and handed her to me. The baby, still conscious, was trying to cry but there was no sound. I remembered my training: Assessment. Her airway was blocked. She couldn't breathe. I opened her mouth up as wide as I could to see if I could see an obstruction. There it was, but it was deep in her throat. I remembered my instructor in the academy saying, "Do not conduct a finger sweep unless you know you can remove the item. You can further lodge the item in the throat."

I transferred the baby to my left arm, face down, ensuring I had her neck and head supported. Tilted her body downward and performed five strikes in between her shoulder blades.

First strike. *Slap*. Too soft, I thought. It's different hitting a real baby.

Second strike. *Whack*. That felt right.

Third, fourth, fifth. *Whack, whack, whack*. I heard a sound. It wasn't a cry, but definitely a sound came from the baby. My heart rate quickened. *Assess again. There it is.* The culprit had been dislodged slightly. *I can get that*, I thought. *No, do five more strikes*. My head noise was loud but my thought process was clear and I was calm. The baby's eyes fixated on mine, knowing that her life was in my hands. This was the first time a baby had looked at me like that but unfortunately not the last. Holding an infant so young their angel wings were still intact. Sinless. Both of us knowing at that point that her life was in the balance. Entering the gray area. Life and the after-life, in a game of tug a war and the after-life had the momentum. I decided to go for it. Finger swipe…

The tip of my pinky finger felt the object blocking her airway. It was deeper or larger than I'd thought. Focused, I remained calm. I felt my nail lock onto something hard. That was my shot. I took it, pulling on the item. Out it came. A small toy figurine her brother had given her.

A breathy gasp… A look burned into my soul. Followed by the most joyous baby cry. Life had won this tug-of-war. I handed the child back to her mother where she belonged. The mother, overcome with emotions, dropped to her knees, baby in hand, hugging and kissing her child. Speaking quickly in Spanish. I didn't understand a word. But I didn't have to. It was the universal language of *love.* Laughter and chatter from the crowd.

"Fuck, Whocco! You did it, man! That was some crazy shit. How the fuck did you do that?" Nester, never politically correct, asked as the paramedics arrived. The mother and Steven had bonded for life. A bond that shattered fearfulness between strangers, cultural differences, and skin color. It was a good day.

Later that night I was scheduled to meet Mick and G-Man for dinner to discuss an upcoming training event with Jax's group. When I called G-Man to confirm our dinner location I couldn't wait to share my news with him. We settled on a meet time and location. The usual, Mexican food. My favorite. I like everything about Mexican. Chips and salsa. Tacos and a few ice-cold Coronas. After niceties, work drama conversations and our fill of chips and salsa with one Corona in our bellies, G-Man pulled out a toy medal that looked like he'd stolen it from his son's Crackerjack box.

Holding it up high in the air but leaning towards the middle of the table with a whisper, he said, "Officer MacGregor jumped into action, showing poise and courage. His quick thinking, training and courage…"

Mick interrupted him with his own version of a whisper, adding, "You already said courage."

"Oh sorry. Where was I?" G-Man said.

305

"Bravery. Don't they always say bravery?" Mick said, taking another drink of his Corona.

"Yes. And bravery. Saved a life. I hereby award you Officer MacGregor on behalf of the Chief of Police this Life Saving Medal. Applause, please," G-Man said, handing me the plastic medal and shaking my hand. Mick performed his best golf clap. "You are hereby awarded the Life Saving Medal," G-Man finished, sitting back in his seat. "Cheers! Great job."

Mick and G-Man hoisted their Coronas.

"You guys are crazy. But thank you," I said, sincerely appreciating their efforts and humor as the bottles of Corona clashed in the air.

"Hey, you didn't look me in the eye when we cheered! You have to look a man in the eye when you cheer then take a drink," Mick exclaimed as the alcohol in his Irish blood wakened him.

"Well, let's try it again then," I said, laughing and looking him in the eye as we clashed our bottles again and took another swig.

"If you weren't under the sheets, you would have been awarded the medal. But this is the best I can do. Unfortunate. The public will never know what you did," G-Man said.

"It's okay, boss. I like your version better," I said, looking G-Man in the eye with a nod of my head.

"Are we done with this grab-assing? We have work to do," Mick said, with another swig.

G-man shook his head with frustration at Mick before switching gears. "Great job. Seriously. So, what's up with this training? What do you know about it?"

"I don't know much but Jax has been very weird about it. Something is up but I don't know what," I said.

"What makes you say that?" G-Man asked.

"It's Jax. I don't know. He's just been acting weird. I know that not everyone is going or was invited," I said, trying to explain myself, knowing that G-Man and Mick wanted facts, statements, and not my intuition.

"Do you know who's going to be there or who got the invites?" Mick asked.

"The only one I know is going from our group is Tom. The others didn't get the invite and they weren't happy about it. He didn't say, but I believe it's only going to be a small group at the upper range where we trained last time. We're supposed to be there by 9 AM to help set up with a 10 kick-off. He said it's going to be a full day but that was it," I said.

"I know you work that day. Did you get it off?" Mick asked as the waitress walked up to our table to check on us.

"Hey, can we get another round when you get a chance, hun?" Mick asked.

"You got it, boys," the waitress answered.

"No. I didn't get it off. I'm going to see if Sal or Lupe can work it for me. If not, I'll call in sick again," I said.

"What's up with this Lupe girl you keep mentioning? Are you going to come clean with me yet?" Mick asked, on a witch hunt, but G-Man ignored his boyish behavior as always, moving on.

"I know last time you guys trained there you said that we shouldn't cover you," he said with a serious tone. "It was too dangerous. Do you think we should try and cover you this time if Jax is acting weird and your instincts are right?"

It was a great question that I didn't know the answer to. The upper range was very secluded and nearly impossible to cover. It would be a death sentence.

"I looked last time and there really isn't anywhere you guys could cover me from without putting yourselves in danger. Now, if we go to the lower range, which is open to the public, you could cover me there, but Jax said we were going to be on the upper range."

"What do you think is special about this training?" Mick asked.

"I don't even know that anything *is* special about this training. He's just acting a little weird. He hasn't said anything or given me anything. I don't know, maybe I'm wrong," I said, taking a long drink of my fresh Corona. The beer was so cold. Perfect.

"Go with your instinct. I'm not trying to talk you out of anything. I'm just trying to figure out how to cover you for safety reasons and for the investigation. If they are up to something, I want it recorded," G-Man said, taking a drink of his beer.

"I can't do a wire up there. No way," I said.

"Yeah. I know. I would never have you wear a wire where we couldn't cover you," G-Man reiterated what I already knew. "Are you okay if I put a team down at the bottom of the hill so when you guys come out we can document it that way?" he asked.

"Sure. Just don't get burned or bring that other jack wagon that stopped his car in front of Jason's house last time. For f-sake, who was that guy? Did you talk to him?" I said, shaking my head and taking another drink of my Corona.

Mick and G-Man started laughing because they knew exactly what I was referring to. "You're damn right I did. No. I'm not putting that fuckstick on any more of my surveillance teams again. What an idiot," Mick said, ranting, but that was why I liked him. Transparent. Never fake. Loyal as a dog.

"Okay. Let's go with that. Is everyone good with that plan?" G-Man said to the group.

"Hey? I know you say Jax is acting weird and you can't put your finger on it but you don't think there's any chance you're burned do you?" Mick asked me, catching me off guard.

"No way. Not a chance," I said with a laugh.

G-Man focused on my non-verbal behaviors.

"You're following your op-sec protocols. You haven't slipped in any way?" Mick continued to dig, which I appreciated. I knew his heart was in the right place and not trying to catch me dirty.

"I've been solid. There's nothing I can think of," I said.

"Okay. Just don't get complacent. These fuckers are not your friends and will throw you in a ditch," he said.

Kill House

That weekend Tom and I drove up to the training together. The conversation was normal, nothing out of the ordinary for two militia boys heading off to learn how to kill government agents. But today I was tired of talking about the overrunning of the border, government chips implanted in our bodies, guns, black helicopters, the New World Order, abolishment of the constitution, conspiracy theories, preparing for when

309

the balloon goes up and all the other madness that dominated militia circles. Today, I was impatient and I just wanted to get to the training so we could shoot some shit. I was done talking and I needed a reset. That's what I loved about Jax and his group, the Western Marksmen Association. They didn't talk about the madness. They were all about the training and preparing.

Bellies full, the ten hand-picked operators all arrived on time at the upper range. It was a short drive from the public range up a winding road, tucked back in the corner, smaller than the lower range, a flat piece of land surround by dirt mounds on the 2, 3, and 4 sides providing a safe haven from stray bullets. A perfect spot for the kill house. The kill house was constructed of pre-made 4x8 wood panels, made a few months prior and stored in a large container on the range. The wood panels stood upright, mimicking the walls of a house, placed side by side with wood "T's" on the ground to hold the panels upright. The two 4x8 panels, now side-by-side, were attached with two screws, securing them together to form a wall. The process was repeated following a pre-determined floor plan taken from a book. A shell of a 2,500-square-foot home could be completed in about forty-five minutes.

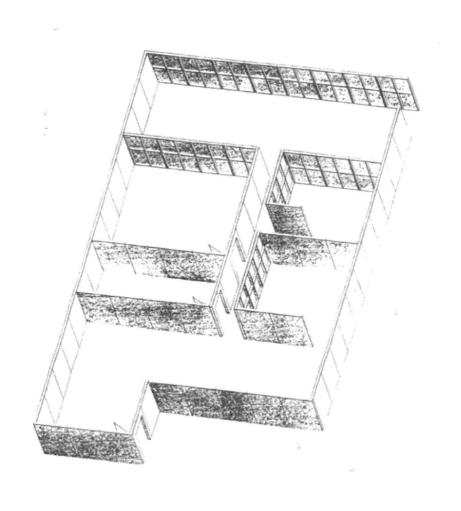

Prior to today's event, Tom and I had attended seven advanced training events with Jax, three held here at the upper range. Jax was amped. It was the first time I'd witnessed at least some version of Jax in go mode, I didn't know why. The attendees were mostly members of the Western Marksmen Association: Jax, Ted (his right-hand man), Jack, Billy, Mark, Richard,

Bob, Tom, Me, and Brian, the confirmed LAPD officer. Ten members. A common number used by SWAT teams.

"Thirty minutes until we brief. Uniform is night ops, black camos, with full load out. Primary and secondary weapons," Jax yelled to the group as everyone nodded in agreement. Any passer-by, of which there weren't any, would assume we were a SWAT team and not a local militia. Militia men standing behind their vehicles changing into battle fatigues and loading magazines. Ten operators dressed in all black uniforms, CAR-15 rifles slung at the ready, locked and loaded with 30-round magazines. Tactical vests with six pouches across the front of each operator's chest holding two 30-round magazines in each pocket, outfitting each militia man with an extra 180 rounds. Every operator with a secondary weapon, a pistol with a tactical light in a thigh rig. Spare secondary magazines lined along the tactical belt of each operator's waistline, outfitting each militia man with an extra 45 rounds. Ted had a first aid kit housed in a second thigh rig pouch on his left leg. Billy was equipped with a sledgehammer in a sling along his back. Bob had a hooligan tool slung on his back; breaching tools for house or building entries.

"Tom! Steven! Did you guys get comms yet?" Ted asked.

"No, we haven't. Not yet," Tom said.

"Come grab these. You'll need them today. Here are two sets. Just make sure that I get them back. Channel five today. Make sure you do a radio check before the briefing," Ted said, handing Tom two radios with earpieces and throat mics.

Twenty minutes later we all gathered around a whiteboard standing on an easel. An irate feeling. If the public only knew. Brian was today's instructor. On the board, each of our names was listed with our designated role in the stack.

"Listen up! Take one and pass it to your team member," Brian called out, handing today's training schedule to Jax. The training agenda was extensive and advanced, broken down into two phases. Phase 1 was on the whiteboard, transitioning into Phase 2, live fire in the kill house.

"Listen up! We're not going to get through all of this today but we will over the next few weeks until we get proficient and cover everything. Today, for the first hour we're going to cover as much as we can of Phase 1, then we'll have a short break and move onto Phase 2: House Work," Brian yelled to the group.

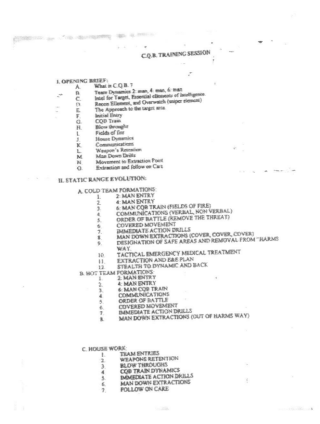

C.Q.B. TRAINING SESSION

I. OPENING BRIEF:
   A. What is C.Q.B. ?
   B. Team Dynamics 2: man, 4: man, 6: man
   C. Intel for Target, Essential elements of Intelligence
   D. Recon Element, and Overwatch (sniper element)
   E. The Approach to the target area
   F. Initial Entry
   G. CQB Team
   H. Blow throughs
   I. Fields of fire
   J. House Dynamics
   K. Communications
   L. Weapon's Retention
   M. Man Down Drills
   N. Movement to Extraction Point
   O. Extraction and follow on Cart

II. STATIC RANGE EVOLUTION:
   A. COLD TEAM FORMATIONS:
     1. 2: MAN ENTRY
     2. 4: MAN ENTRY
     3. 6: MAN CQB TRAIN (FIELDS OF FIRE)
     4. COMMUNICATIONS (VERBAL, NON VERBAL)
     5. ORDER OF BATTLE (REMOVE THE THREAT)
     6. COVERED MOVEMENT
     7. IMMEDIATE ACTION DRILLS
     8. MAN DOWN EXTRACTIONS (COVER, COVER, COVER)
     9. DESIGNATION OF SAFE AREAS AND REMOVAL FROM "HARMS WAY.
     10. TACTICAL EMERGENCY MEDICAL TREATMENT
     11. EXTRACTION AND E&E PLAN
     12. STEALTH TO DYNAMIC AND BACK
   B. HOT TEAM FORMATIONS:
     1. 2: MAN ENTRY
     2. 4: MAN ENTRY
     3. 6: MAN CQB TRAIN
     4. COMMUNICATIONS
     5. ORDER OF BATTLE
     6. COVERED MOVEMENT
     7. IMMEDIATE ACTION DRILLS
     8. MAN DOWN EXTRACTIONS (OUT OF HARMS WAY)

   C. HOUSE WORK:
     1. TEAM ENTRIES
     2. WEAPONS RETENTION
     3. BLOW THROUGHS
     4. CQB TRAIN DYNAMICS
     5. IMMEDIATE ACTION DRILLS
     6. MAN DOWN EXTRACTIONS
     7. FOLLOW ON CARE

Jax, holding his rifle, which was attached to a three-point sling across his chest, trigger finger along the frame, chimed in, "Start to get your minds right. Today's training will be live fire. No fuck-ups. Assume any targets inside are enemy combatants and are to be dealt with accordingly. It's a *kill* house, not a *fun* house today, gentlemen."

Brian nodded and started the whiteboard training, going over how to clear a house; dynamic versus stealth. Police and special forces tactics mixed. The training was thorough and more advanced than the tactics training I'd received in the police academy. He even gave the group handouts, explaining further with live demonstrations.

CUTTING THE PIE

In urban settings, architectural surroundings will dictate the nature of your tactics and the methods used to clear a particular structure. There are two basic types of tactical movement: stealth movement and dynamic movement. Each one is a valuable tool for use in clearing a building. Generally, stealth movement is used when we want to literally "sneak up" on an adversary. Dynamic movement is generally used after the adversary has been located and we've chosen to make contact. This method is favored for hostage rescue as well as "drug raids" by some agencies.

Searching is almost always done with the stealth method, and that is what this particular article will discuss. Please understand that these are simply guidelines, not commandments. Tactically speaking, the only real commandment is to be flexible.

Clearing a building is greatly simplified if we think of the search geometrically in terms of "cutting the angles" and "breaking the planes." Angles are the lines of sight/fire that we obtain as we move through a structure. These angles are available both ways, meaning that any line of sight/fire you have into a danger area, an enemy within has the same angle on you. Breaking a plane means reaching, and eventually passing, through a portal into a new uncleared space. For example, as we enter an uncleared room, we have entered onto a geometric plane whose immediate vastness cannot be "covered" in all directions by a single man. The number of people on your "team" will more or less dictate the level of risk as well as the level of speed during a clearing operation.

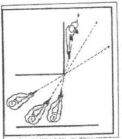

Some architectural situations will present only one danger area at a time, such as a simple corner. The corner is one of the most basic and often encountered building features—and also one of the most dangerous. We simply cannot see what is around that corner without exposing ourselves to the dangers beyond it. Various tacticians have developed ways to deal with corners.

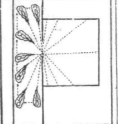

One of these is the use of a small handheld mirror to visually scan the uncleared space while remaining behind cover. This will sometimes work, but a great deal of practice is required to accurately hold and scan with the mirror. A big problem that I see with the mirror (no pun intended) is that the searcher's eyes will be on the mirror itself and not on the possible source of the danger. Additionally, if there does happen to be a boogie man hiding around the corner waiting for you, sticking that mirror into the uncleared space has just announced your presence and the presence of your partner and/or enticed him. A third problem with mirrors is that, like most "crutches," it will never be there when you really need it.

The second method promulgated by many tactical thinkers is the "quick peek." My colleagues call it the "quick death" for its user! This method involves snuggling up to the corner in question and quickly sticking your face into the uncleared space in hopes of seeing something important, and then pulling it back quickly. This is akin to testing a seatbelt by deliberately crashing into a wall. The main problem with the quick peek is that we simply cannot see enough of the uncleared space to be of any use. Even if we did see something of what lay beyond that corner, we would eventually still need to negotiate the corner and move into the uncleared space. Why pay for the same "real estate" twice? Also, if there is a hostile individual

314

Over two hours of whiteboard training the group was amped and wanted to go hot, but Ted held onto the reins like a jockey before the final turn. After a short break, we went back at it. Four hours of dry runs inside the kill house. Weapons at the ready, but not loaded. Drilling tactics, each operator's role, shooting area of responsibilities, target acquisition, blow-throughs, man down drills, team extraction, running the walls, button hooks. Perfecting movements, building trust as an operational team. Jax, the operational team leader, was preaching. Yelling. *"Just do your job!"* At times calling out specific operators, *"Pull your head out of your ass!"*

Everyone looked proficient to me. Tom was the weakest link by far, but Jax didn't ridicule him the way he did his own team. On our last break for the day, my mind wandered. I was tired. The thirty pounds of gear after seven or so hours of intense training was weighing on me, both physically and mentally. What were we doing? These boys were just gun nuts and wannabe cops. Why would Brian teach them police tactics? What was his motivation? Why were they training so intensely? Mission focused? I was ready to go home. There were too many puzzle pieces missing and I was done for the day mentally.

I began to build the fire in my chest through breathing techniques I learned from my martial arts days. A technique to focus your mind and increase your adrenaline levels. Inhale through your nose, blow it out through your mouth, rocking forward and backwards slightly opening the lungs. On the fifth breath, hold it and swallow your breath. Feel the breath travel down into your belly, igniting it. The pressure. Continue to hold your breath as long as possible. Don't breathe. Finishing with a slow exhale out of your mouth. Feel the core of your body temperature rise and jump-start the production of adrenaline. Repeat the process.

"Lock and load. The range is hot. I repeat, the range is hot. Lock and load. Meet at the jump off in five minutes," Jax yelled to the group, who were spread out near their vehicles, many chewing on snacks. The group was amped for our first live entry into the kill house of the day, or what was left of it. "Listen up! We rearranged the layout of the kill house. It's not the same layout we were doing on the walkthroughs. There are enemy combatants inside. Every target is a green light. I repeat: no friendlies inside. Are there any questions?"

We all stacked up at the jump off location, conducted our last checks, comms, weapons, waiting for the squeeze. Another quick chamber check, exposing the brass of a .223 caliber round as I felt the squeeze on my leg from Tom who was positioned behind me. The go sign. I was positioned fourth in the stack as we began to move towards the front door of the kill house. Jack was the point and Brian was rear security. The first and last operators in the stack.

Jax called for a stealth entry over the radio. He was most likely going to button hook, I thought, trying to predict his entry technique. We reached the front door and Jax held his left hand in the air with a closed fist, signaling the team to hold. Brian had peeled off the stack to cover the two side. Bob held, covering the front window, which was a cut-out in the wood panels covered by a black sheet blocking the view inside. Everyone was doing their jobs. The last of the day's sunlight was parting, making it a low light entry. Raising the difficulty level.

I struggled to remember who was where in the stack. The donning of balaclava masks during the last break didn't help. Face or head warmers. Identity killers. Hooded masks with only the eyes cut out. My heart rate was elevated, just as I wanted, but I was focused. In the zone. The entry team was set. I felt the squeeze on my leg and passed it forward, squeezing Jax's leg which was positioned in front of me. He nodded in acknowledgement, passing it forward.

Suddenly we were on the move. Jack button hooked through the front door like I thought he would. Ted on his heels, followed by Jax and myself then Tom filing into the first room. Jack running the first wall. Ted peeled off, running the other wall, and Jax and I entered the room just past the kill zone and held. I saw two targets towards the back of the room behind a sofa and wondered why Ted hadn't fired yet.

Bang, bang! Ted fired a pair.

Bang, bang! Jack followed, firing a pair of his own.

"Stop! Stop! Weapons down. Admin hold!" Ted yelled. "Jack. You got to make that shot sooner. As soon as the target presents itself, put that fucker down! Every target in here is an enemy combatant trying to kill you! Don't keep running the fucking wall like a hamster until you get to the target and then engage. We'll be dead! And hit your fucking target. Run it again."

We headed back to the jump off location to run it again. I'd never seen Ted angry before. After four plus hours of walkthroughs he expected and demanded better. So did Jax.

After six runs, Jax called for a water break to rearrange the house and give the team a breather. The team was frustrated. Jack was struggling, only hitting the target one out of six runs. As a team, we still hadn't gotten past the first room and many of us had yet to fire a shot all day.

The water break was longer than anyone anticipated. Ted, Brian, and Jax were having a long discussion near the front door of the kill house.

"Hey, Steven. I'm sorry but I have to go. I didn't know the training was going to last this long," Tom said to me during the break.

"No worries. Let's go then. I'm tired too," I said. Relieved. I was getting cold and it had been a long day. As the impromptu meeting was adjourned, Jax and Ted announced that training was over, but a few of them were going to stay and do a few more runs for fun.

"Hey, Steven. Can you stay or do you have to go with Tom?" Jax asked.

"No. I have to go. He's my ride. Sorry," I said, ready to head down the hill.

"I can give you a ride if you want to stay," Jax said.

An odd gesture, I thought, processing his request. My apartment was 35 miles out of his way.

"Hey, stay if you can. We need you," the other guys called out.

"Seriously," Jax said. "Either I or someone else can give you a ride. It's no trouble. Promise."

Jax was self-centered and didn't do anything for others. There had to be something in it for him but I struggled to understand what it was.

"Sure, if you don't mind. Let me grab my stuff first," I said, walking over to Tom's car. I had a bad feeling in the pit of my stomach.

"Hey, Jax. I'm heading out too. I've had enough fun for today. I'm just not on my game," Jack said, frustrated with his performance.

"I understand. Sorry for yelling at you earlier. You'll get it. I know you will, man. Can you do me a favor and lock the security gate at the bottom of the hill? I have my key," Jax told him and they embraced in a man hug.

318

That left eight operators – over-achievers, or just looking to blow off some steam? Most likely the latter, I thought.

"Toys?" Mark yelled to Jax.

Jax hesitated briefly. "Yeah. Let's do it!"

There was an excitement in the air when he agreed.

Jax placed two paper targets at the end of the range adjacent to the kill house.

Mark grabbed his rifle. "Going hot! Going hot!" he announced to the range, taking a shooting stance. Leaning more forward than normal. A rapid sound of gunfire that I'd never heard before was unleashed. Flames flying out of the front of the rifle lighting up the darkening sky.

Bang, bang, bang, bang, bang, bang, bang, bang.

Bang, bang, bang, bang, bang, bang, bang, bang.

Bang, bang, bang, bang, bang, bang, bang, bang.

Bang, bang, bang, bang, bang, bang, bang.

The hillside was getting ripped apart. Violently. Dirt, rocks, flying into the air as each round impacted the hillside. Smoke and the smell of gunfire filled the air. Mark let out a scream, "Hoorah!" He looked at his rifle barrel. Smoke was still coming out of the end. The barrel had a slight glow.

Toys was the code word for fully automatic weapons. Jax's team, the inner circle which I now knew I was not part of, was equipped with fully automatic weapons.

"Do you feel better now, Mark?" Ted yelled, removing his ear protection.

"I do actually. Thank you!" he said with a huge smile on his face.

Billy was up next ...

Bang, bang, bang, bang, bang, bang, bang, bang.

Bang, bang, bang, bang, bang, bang, bang, bang.

Bang, bang, bang, bang, bang, bang, bang, bang.

Bang, bang, bang, bang, bang, bang, bang.

"Control your muzzle, Billy. For fuck sake! Don't let it climb on you like that," Jax yelled.

Jax went next. Then Ted. Followed by Bob and Richard. Brian was the only one not to fire his weapon in full auto. I wondered if his rifle had been converted. An undeniable violation of California's strict gun laws. A felony.

"Hey, Steven. Do you want to give it a go?" Jax asked me.

"Sure!" I said, getting up from the tree stump I'd been sitting on.

"Here. Use mine," Jax said, handing me his rifle. "Do you know how this works?"

"No, I don't," I said, excited to shoot full auto.

"It's the same as your rifle except the selector switch just has one more position. Safe, then semi-auto, then the third position is full-auto. The barrel will have a tendency to climb on you high and right so make sure you lock in a good shooting stance," he said, standing behind me with his right hand on my shoulder.

Bang, bang, bang, bang.

Bang, bang, bang, bang.

"Let it fly! Keep your finger on the trigger. It's okay. Let it fly," Jax yelled at me.

Bang, bang...

I let it fly just like Jax said, firing twenty-three .223 caliber rounds in a matter of seconds. It was powerful. Violent. Exhilarating and so destructive. But the pit in my stomach was still there. I couldn't shake it. It wasn't something I'd eaten. It wasn't a cramp. It wasn't nerves. It was animalistic. Primal. Something was wrong.

"Hey, are you guys up for running the house?" Jax yelled to the group and everyone agreed.

The feeling in my stomach blindsided me. It came on so fast. Unlike in the movies. I had no protection. All the warning signs ran through my head in an instant:

- Shooting automatic weapons.
- Jack locking the gate.
- The group demanding I stay.
- Jax offering me a ride.
- The training was so late.

"Steven. Are you up to run point?" Jax asked me.

"Sure," I hesitantly agreed. Rolling with it but on high alert.

"Mark, two. Ted, three. I'll be four. Brian, five. Billy, six. Richard, seven, and Bob you're in the rear," Jax called out.

"Jax. What do you think about night vision goggles?" Ted asked.

Jax looked up into the sky before answering. "No. Not yet. It's too light out for them right now. Hey. No jump off location on these. We're starting at the house, just stack up. Same rules of engagement."

I was point. The first operator through the door. Even though we were just screwing around, to blow off some steam. Or at least that's what Jax was saying. I knew he'd put me there for a reason and it felt bad. Then

321

I remembered that Jack hadn't been able to get the job done earlier and so maybe Jax was testing me and it wasn't as bad as I thought. I had either gained huge strides within the group when they'd exposed me to their automatic weapons or the gig was up and they were going to kill me in a training exercise. Either way, it was a personal growth opportunity. My Tom Brady moment.

I felt Mark squeeze my thigh from behind. I nodded in acknowledgement. Richard, standing on the opposite side of the stack, opened and pushed the door inward. I moved quickly, passing through the threshold of the front door where I was confronted with an immediate target at my 12 o'clock about six feet away. Mark was in my hip pocket. My rifle at the low ready I brought it up on target, finger on the trigger. The target was a metal plate. I didn't fire, but Mark unleashed his weapon positioned directly off my right shoulder. The selector switch still in the third position: fully automatic.

Bang, bang, bang, bang, bang, bang... I felt the rapid burst of air hitting my right cheek with each round fired in rapid succession. The heat. The flashing. I felt something hit my forehead with force. It burned, but wasn't painful. Continuing straight, target acquired off to my right, in the corner behind a couch. Moving, I pressed off two shots and continued to run the wall.

Bang. Bang.

Mark button hooked to the right and pressed off two shots at the second target he'd seen in the other corner.

Bang. Bang. It was semi-auto.

Jax motioned for me to hold the hallway with Ted as Mark and Brian set up to clear a bedroom.

322

"Moving," I heard over the radio. Focused on my job, the hallway, I didn't look.

"All clear. Coming out," echoed in my earpiece.

I felt a squeeze. "Moving," I said, crisscrossing through the threshold of the next doorway. Another bedroom. Ted followed my lead.

Bang, bang. I fired two rounds at a paper silhouette. A gunman holding a lady hostage. The room was clear.

"All clear," I said.

"Hold," Jax said.

"Moving," I heard Billy say over the radio.

Bang. Bang.

Bang. Bang.

"All clear," I heard Billy say.

"Hold," Jax said. He motioned for Ted and I to move forward to set up for the next room. As we moved into the hallway, Mark and Brian entered a room. No gunfire.

"All clear," I heard Mark say.

Bob was positioned in the first room holding our ground and covering our six.

Ted and I moved forward, setting up to clear the back of the kill house.

"Coming out," Mark said. He and Brian positioned themselves behind us.

Something was in my right eye. I tried to wipe it away. My eye was burning. I couldn't see out of it. My vision was blurry and I felt light-headed. The squeeze. I moved.

Bang. Bang.

Bang. Bang.

Bang. Bang.

There were multiple targets and shooters.

"All clear."

"Stand down, men. Nice run. Meet at the front of the house," Jax said over the radio.

The kill house was filled with dust and the smell of gunfire in the air and blood on the ground.

"Steven. You're bleeding! Man, you're bleeding! Oh fuck. He's shot," Brian said. I felt the pain in my forehead.

"Take your hood off! Take his hood off! Medic," Brian called out in a panic. I expected him to be calmer as an LAPD officer and former special ops guy. My hood was soaked with blood which was now running down my face. It was warm compared to the cold breeze hitting my face. The pain increased. My mind conducted an internal assessment of the damage. I'd been shot in the head. My right ear was ringing with a high-pitched tone and I couldn't hear out of it. I couldn't see out of my right eye. Everything else seemed fine. Strangely, I wasn't scared. I was pissed. I knew something bad was going to happen.

Mark was sitting on the ground with his back up against the kill house. I couldn't tell his mood but it wasn't what I'd expected from a guy who'd just shot me.

Ted, the militia team's medic, grabbed his first aid kit and began to ask me a series of questions.

"Do you know where you are?"

"Are you light headed?"

"Do you feel sick?"

324

"Are you hurt anywhere else?"

"How many fingers do I have up?"

My forehead was peppered with lead fragments that had pierced through my nylon hood. Nine holes in total that Ted could count. I didn't know that a person's forehead could bleed so much. It turns out that your face and forehead are lined with a plethora of tiny blood vessels. Who knew?

"This is gonna hurt, but I need to clean it so I can see what's going on," Ted said and I nodded.

He doused a clean bandage with hydrogen peroxide and began cleaning the holes in my head, probing how deep they were. The hydrogen peroxide hurt like hell. A procedure once preached, now scoffed at. There was no talk of calling 911 or transporting me to a hospital.

"Give me a light! Lie down for me," Ted said, in go mode.

I lay back with my head in the dirt. It was cold on my neck. My rifle, attached to the three-point sling, still loaded, lay across my chest. I remember seeing the moon. It was full. My right hand was on my pistol. I remember lowering the holster safety so I could draw it quickly if needed. My will to survive remained intact. A bright light blinded me and it wasn't inviting in this case.

"Oh. Fuck me," I heard Ted say.

My forehead was throbbing. Ted began probing – or digging, it felt like – lead fragments out of my frontal bone. I could feel the tweezers on my skull, grabbing tissue or bone particles with each tug. One by one he removed the lead fragments from my forehead. The pain was excruciating. Far more severe than when I'd broken my wrist during a martial arts tournament. It was nauseating, so much so that experience was telling me I was about to lose consciousness. My mind turned to G-Man and Mick. If I died, their lives would never be the same. Death notifications were part of the job. All policemen know it. The public never hears about it. But a death notification to the parent or spouse of one of your partners; your responsibility is on another level. A cross you will always bear.

"Steven! Steven. Stay with me," Ted yelled, but his speech was slow to me. My hands and feet were starting to tingle. It was the last thing I remember.

"Steven! Steven! Oh fuck, he's out," Ted said.

"Is he dead?" Jax asked.

Book three – the final chapter coming soon.

Made in the USA
Las Vegas, NV
08 February 2023

67154274R00179